Leading Innovation and Change in the Health Service

Leading Innovation and Change in the Health Service

A book of readings

Edited by

George Boak: Senior Lecturer in Management & Leadership at
York St John College

and

Helen Jones: Director of the Centre for Leadership Development at the
University of York.

Kingsham

First published in 2002
by Kingsham Press

Oldbury Complex
Marsh Lane
Easthampnett
Chichester, West Sussex
PO18 OJW
United Kingdom

© 2002, George Boak & Helen Jones

Typeset in AGaramond

Printed and bound by
MPG Books
Bodmin
Cornwall
United Kingdom

ISBN: 1-904235-01-8

British Library Cataloging in Publication Data
A catalogue record of this book is available from the British Library

Boak, George & Jones, Helen

The Editors

George Boak is a Senior Lecturer in Management and Leadership at St John College, York. He has worked as a management development consultant since 1987, concentrating mainly on leadership development for senior and middle managers and developing flexible learning systems. He has worked with middle managers from a range of different industries, including manufacturing, banking, local and central government and the health service. He joined the College in 1997 and also continues to work as an independent consultant. He is author of *A Complete Guide to Learning Contracts* and co-author of *Mental Models for Managers*.

Helen Jones is Director of the Centre for Leadership Development at the University of York since it came into being in 1995. During the 1980s, she was Director of Training and Education at the Centre for Personal Construct Psychology in London. On moving to York in 1987 she worked in the NHS as an Organisation Development Specialist with Yorkshire Regional Health Authority. She was particularly responsible for directing a nationally recognised programme for Doctors and Managers during this time. Together with Mary Connor at York St. John College, she designed the MA in Leading Innovation and Change.

She continues to work both for the University of York and as an independent consultant and psychotherapist.

Contributors

Carole Langrick is Director of Health Systems Performance at Tees Health Authority.

Dr Ian Cameron is a Consultant in Public Health Medicine at Leeds Health Authority.

Stephanie Stanwick is the Chief Executive Officer of Dartford, Gravesham and Swanley Primary Care Trust.

John Kitson is Organisational Development Manager at Tees Health Authority.

Thelma Holland is the Chief Executive of the Cornwall & Isles of Scilly Health Authority.

Lynda Hanson is the Director of Operations and Facilities at Calderdale and Huddersfield NHS Trust.

Judith Holbrey works in Performance Management at the NHS Executive in the Northern and Yorkshire Region.

Andrea Hopkins is Director of Nursing and Primary Care Development for Wakefield West Primary Care Trust.

Mark Crowther is an Organisation Development Consultant who has worked for the NHS for 14 years.

Dr Mary Courtney is a Consultant Psychiatrist at the Barnsley Community and Priority Services Trust.

Dr Tony Dearden is a Consultant Psychiatrist and the Associate Medical Director (Old Age Psychiatry) Leeds Community and Mental Health Services (Teaching) NHS Trust.

Martin Jones is an Executive Director of Operations and Performance Management at a Welsh NHS Trust.

Dr Mike Porte is a Consultant Radiologist and the Medical Director at York Health Services NHS Trust.

Jayne Barnes is Executive Nurse Director of the West Yorkshire NHS Direct service and Director of NHS Professionals.

Karen Picking is an Organisation Development Consultant. She was the Director of Organisation Development, South Tees Acute Hospitals NHS Trust from 1991–2000.

Acknowledgements

We should like to thank all the people with whom we have worked on the MA Leading Innovation and Change programme. The participants deserve recognition for their tremendous achievements in balancing the opportunities and demands of course work not only with the great challenges of change that accompany leadership roles in the health service today, but also with the need to have some personal and family life. Working with the participants on this programme has been a most rewarding and enlightening experience for us.

We should also like to thank our colleagues who have helped to design and deliver the programme, and in particular Mary Connor, John Bennett and Chris Holmes, fellow members of the core programme team.

George Boak
Helen Jones
September 2001

For further details of the MA in Leading Innovation and Change, contact:

Centre for Leadership Development
The University of York
The White Hart
Cold Bath Road
Harrogate, HG2 ONF

Telephone: 01423 507771
Fax: 01423 509304
e.mail: hmj2@york.ac.uk

Contents

Introduction

This book is for anyone who is interested in the leadership and management of the National Health Service at the start of the 21st century. At a time when the NHS, the biggest organisation in the UK, is facing massive change through modernisation, the authors represent the positive and constructive approaches many clinical leaders and senior managers are taking to become better leaders. It is hoped that the book will contribute to a better understanding of the need to work with complexity and change in a radically different way.

The separate chapters of this book have been contributed by practitioners who are – or who have recently been – senior managers and professionals in the National Health Service.

They have been asked to write for people like themselves – practical, experienced contributors to the NHS, who know there are no instant solutions, no magic cures, and are prepared to spend a little time standing back for a moment from the bustle of immediate demands to understand the patterns and the problems and the possibilities of leadership in the health service.

Clinicians and managers in the UK healthcare system have been subjected to a relentless stream of changes imposed by one political initiative or another over the past twenty years. This has made some practitioners passive. Even at senior levels in some organisations we find managers who say: 'I can't influence strategy. I can't lead. I can't innovate. I'm told what to do.'

In these challenging times, we believe that healthcare organisations need more than ever people who are prepared to take what opportunities they can find to lead, rather than just to follow, who are prepared to develop the new ideas and practices that will shape their organisations. These leaders are needed at every level. Those at the top of the organisation's structures have the added responsibility of creating sufficient space for leaders at lower levels to be able to take action.

Effective leadership is not the business of minutely directing the behaviour of others, as many of our contributors make clear. Effective leadership in modern healthcare is more about working well in partnership, influencing others and also being prepared to influence, working cooperatively rather than in competition.

The first chapter of this book explores in more detail the themes of leadership, innovation and change.

In the second chapter, Carole Langrick assesses the capabilities of the new Strategic Health Authorities to act as strategic leaders. In the third chapter, Ian Cameron explores the theme of leadership from the primary care perspective.

The 1997 White Paper required healthcare organisations to work in partnership with one another. Stephanie Stanwick has developed the outline of a new model of effective partnership working, which emphasises the importance of understanding how to work across different cultures. John Kitson has investigated the individual competencies that are needed for effective partnership working between healthcare organisations and local authority managers, and Thelma Holland provides a case study of the early stages of a partnership between two large Trusts, using a partnership audit to assess progress.

Lynda Hanson demonstrates the potential benefits of multidisciplinary team working in primary care, while Judith Holbrey describes the team-based change project that led her to adopt a participative approach to change throughout her Trust, and considers the far-from-straightforward connections between participation and empowerment. On a similar theme, Andrea Hopkins provides a case study of the empowerment of nurses in a Trust in the context of clinical governance, and contrasts this with best practice in the USA.

The idea of a 'learning organisation' has been used for several years to describe an organisation that would be well equipped to deal with change. Mark Crowther explores the culture of a Trust and links it to a capacity for organisational learning. Mary Courtney detects three broad cultures within a Trust, at director, manager and clinician levels.

Tony Dearden focuses on the area of how doctors and managers make decisions together, where each considers themselves most influential, and where each group would like more power. Martin Jones explores a particular dimension of leadership within a Trust – the relationships between managers and their team members.

Implementing strategy in the NHS is rarely a straightforward task, and Mike Porte illustrates this is in his case study of three critical incidents that shaped clinical governance within his Trust.

Jayne Barnes is a Director of NHS Direct in West Yorkshire, and Director of NHS Professionals, and in her chapter she reflects on her experiences of building new organisations. Finally, Karen Picking describes how creative collaboration has been used to achieve innovation and complex inter-organisational change.

Apart from the chapters by George, Jayne and Karen, the contributions are all based on research the authors carried out as part of an executive Master's degree programme which, since 1995, has been delivered by a partnership between the Centre for Leadership Development in York University, and York St John College, a college of Leeds University. The aim of the programme is to provide opportunities for leaders of innovation and change to work together on issues which will have significant impact within their organisations, in order to enhance both individual and organisational potential. Short research projects are undertaken as part of this programme, usually over a six-month period. Given the short time scale, field research is generally restricted to small surveys or a limited number of depth interviews. The findings described by our contributors are, therefore, suggestive rather than conclusive but in each case we believe they are worthy of further consideration.

We believe the writers have succeeded in combining their practical understanding of leadership and change in the health service with the rigour of systematic inquiry into areas that are of interest to everyone involved with the modernisation of the National Health Service. These people know the NHS and are well acquainted with the fickleness of change management. They demonstrate that the real leaders of change in the NHS must be those at the leading edge of professional practice.

CHAPTER ONE

Change, innovation and leadership

George Boak

> I want nothing less than the re-invention of the NHS – what it does, the way it runs and how it is organised
>
> Secretary of State for Health 2000

This chapter provides a brief introduction to the key themes of this book – leadership, innovation and change, and the relation between the three. In particular, for the National Health Service, it considers the drivers of change, the nature of innovation, and the scope for leadership.

Change

> This is the world of white water where we have to change to survive
>
> White, Hodgson and Crainer 1996

In many organisations in the developed world life has undergone rapid, radical and seemingly continual change in recent years. It seems, on looking back, as though the past provided more stability and certainty – although this may be no more than the soothing effect of hindsight. Nevertheless, over the past ten years change has come to seem not an occasional transition between two different stable conditions, but in itself a normal state of affairs.

In the private sector, the two main drivers of change have been competitive pressure and the opportunities presented by new technology.

Information and communication technology, in particular, has enabled companies to change their ways of working, to reduce costs and increase volumes, and achieve results at greater and greater speed. With the invention of the PC in 1981, and the development of the WWWeb ten years later, whole new industries have come suddenly into being. Ambitious organisations have created new ways of communicating with customers, partners and suppliers, and competitive pressure has then driven their rivals to follow suit.

For the public sector, technology offers similar opportunities. In the Health Service, information technology can speed up all the old processes of filing and communicating information – although major IT projects can be fraught with problems. A new branch of the health service – NHS Direct – has been made possible only through the application of modern information technology. More specific health care technologies also support telemedicine, new scanning and diagnostic machinery, new surgical procedures, new pharmaceutical treatments.

Rather than competition, for the NHS the other main immediate driver of change is the government of the day.

The NHS Plan (2000) described the NHS as 'a 1940s system operating in a 21st century world', before signalling a range of reforming measures, including new directions, new values and principles, and new structures and systems.

Although the NHS was admittedly created in the 1940s, it has been subject to politically-led reforms at regular intervals ever since, particularly over the past twenty years.

The Conservative governments of 1979–97 created competitive pressures in parts of the public sector, with the idea that these would emulate the beneficial effects of competition in the private sector – rewarding efficiency and effectiveness, penalising waste and profligacy. In the health service, internal markets were created between 1991 and 1994, with some healthcare organisations cast as 'purchasers' and other as 'providers'.

The Labour government signalled the end of the internal market for health in 1997, and emphasised partnership and cooperation rather than competition, with an aim of creating an integrated health and social care system focused on the individual needs of patients and carers. This represents a radical change of direction. It has been accompanied by new measures designed to monitor and improve performance.

Governments have also sought to change the managerial style of the NHS. The recommendations of the Griffiths Report in 1983 led to the introduction of a clearly defined general management function designed to unify responsibility for activities in healthcare organisations – and wrest control of the service from the decisions of individual medics (Harrison and Pollitt 1994). This new managerial cadre introduced resource management, objective setting and the establishment of performance management systems.

The present Government, with an initiative that places ultimate responsibility for medical outcomes with senior management, is attempting to make managers and clinicians work more closely together to provide a quality service (DoH 1997, 1998, 2000). An emphasis on patient needs is accompanied by a call for dismantling traditional demarcation lines between roles and, as in many private sector organisations, creating flexible teams that cross organisational and professional boundaries.

Changes in technology, and the will of the government of the day, are far from being the only drivers for change in the health service, of course. Other factors include increased consumerism, together with a capacity for some consumers of healthcare to be much better informed about medical matters than in the past (a capacity much enhanced by the Internet) and a greater disposition on the part of patients and carers to make complaints about poor service, and even to take legal action. Changing demographics form an underlying, inexorable driver for change, as an ageing population is in need of more services of different kinds.

Within hospital Trusts at the time of writing, taskforces of managers and clinicians are working on a raft of initiatives that include Modernisation, Clinical Governance, Performance Management, and partnerships with other organisations in the health and social care community.

The degree of change at present for many in the health service is exhausting. Every alteration to structures and systems required by central government means widespread changes in job roles. Some posts – and some entire organisations – disappear; new posts are offered for competition. This process is often preceded by months of uncertainty and ambiguity about what, exactly, will disappear or come into being. Every new initiative launched by central government means that throughout the health service managers and professionals will be called upon to take on new duties and tackle new challenges.

Innovation

> The gap between what can be imagined and what can be accomplished has never been smaller

Hamel 2000

A number of writers on organisational strategy have encouraged private sector companies to make innovation the engine of their corporate strategy. Lasting competitiveness will only be achieved through innovative change – not by chasing increased efficiency or continually driving down costs (Hamel and Prahalad 1994; Porter 1996; Hamel 2000).

Innovation in the health service is not only seen in the new procedures and treatments produced by continuing medical research, but also in the new organisations and the new ways of working prompted by central government. But, given the degree of direction by central government, how much scope is there for innovation by the managers and professionals who work within the NHS?

A simple view of strategy is that it is set at the top of the organisation – or in the case of the NHS, outside the organisation, by the political leaders of the day – and then implemented by the lower orders. It is certainly true that in some areas of NHS activity, where precise targets have been set by central government, the only remaining questions are about *how* to implement, *how* to achieve.

In other areas of activity, however, broad strategic directions are set from on high, and there is more scope for manoeuvre (at least at first). We will have Clinical Governance, say the politicians – but no one knows (yet) what it will look like or how it will work. Health and social care will work in partnership, say the politicians – but we're not sure quite how that will come about. We have an idea for a service called NHS Direct – can you show us how it might work? These 'umbrella strategies' allow

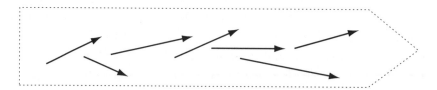

Figure 1: Umbrella strategy and individual initiatives, from Mintzberg and Waters 1985

scope for individual initiative and innovation in creating projects that go in the broad direction that has been indicated, but may also achieve specific local aims that are valued by the innovator.

Even where the scope for inventing new projects is limited, managers and professionals are challenged to think creatively and to innovate as they implement central government's will because:

- they face significant barriers to achieving some of the targets they are set, and must find new ways around, or over, or through these barriers
- they are setting off into uncharted waters in pursuit of some of the targets they are set – the achievement of clinical governance, and the creation of integrated services, for example – and they will need to innovate and learn as they go

And even where healthcare organisations appear to be achieving adequate results, there may still be scope for innovation because there may be a way of achieving even better results, if only they can conceive of it. (Edward de Bono calls this a state where innovation is 'blocked by openness'.)

In the absence of obvious problems, opportunities for innovation can be uncovered by:

- constant constructive questioning of current aims and methods
- providing scope for front line staff to suggest changes
- greater awareness of achievements elsewhere, both within and without the international health care system.

Uncovering opportunities for innovation is one of the roles of an effective leader.

Leadership

> Leadership is about achieving change through changing the way people think about what is desirable and possible. In other words, leadership is about setting direction – often new directions – and initiating changes.
>
> A Zaleznik 1977

What do we mean by leadership? I asked a group of young medical consultants in September 2001 to say what 'leading people' meant to them, and they suggested the following list of leadership activities:

- decision making
- taking responsibility
- setting a good example
- supporting the team
- taking the team with you
- motivation
- matching style to situation
- vision

For most of the twentieth century, leadership in organisations was taken to mean the relationship between managers and their teams – their 'subordinates' or 'direct reports' – and much time and energy was spent on studying the effects of different styles of leadership, whether directive, consultative, supportive, participative or empowering. It was generally agreed that different circumstances favoured different styles, but that a participative style was likely to win more commitment than a directive 'command and control' style.

During the late 1970s and 1980s a different model of leadership emerged, which still dominates much of the thinking about how effective leaders behave. Known as 'transformational leadership', it consists of several strands, but we can summarise the core ideas by saying: 'Leadership means innovating, and achieving change. Leaders do this by changing people's ideas and attitudes. They succeed in winning the commitment of others by communicating a desirable vision of what they should all work to achieve'.

To emphasise the essential connection between leadership and change, transformational leadership is sometimes contrasted with 'management' –the business of implementation, or simply maintaining operations (Zaleznik 1977, Bennis and Nanus 1985). As Bennis and Nanus say:

> Managers are people who do things right and leaders are people who do the right things.

'Management', so described, is not unimportant – but there is a great danger that organisations will be 'over-managed and under-led' (Kotter 1990).

Transformational leadership is different from 'transactional leadership', which motivates people not by winning their commitment to a vision, but more by the promise of tangible rewards – such as pay and promotion (MacGregor Burns 1978). The importance of the visionary dimension of transformational leadership originally derived from a study of inspirational politicians, who by oratory and personal example attempt to win the commitment of the masses. It appealed to chief executives of large organisations, who feel a similar need to win the commitment of their mass workforce.

The influential writings of Tom Peters and Bob Waterman in the 1980s lent weight to the value of a transformational leadership style. Their research emphasised the importance of leaders inspiring people through vision and values, rather than controlling them through rules and procedures. Inspiration will always release more energy than commands and controls.

How much scope is there for transformational leadership in a health service strongly governed by central government initiatives? One chief executive, speaking in a seminar group, summed up the position in a credible way when she said: 'Leadership in the health service means not only making sure you hit all the targets you are set, but also bringing people along with a coherent agenda of your own.' Hitting all the targets gives you freedom to carry on in the role with the minimum of interference: then you can get on with really being a leader.

Research on transformational leadership has also helped innovators and change agents at different levels of organisations everywhere. Whereas transactional leadership and ideas about leadership style are only relevant where a leader has the formal authority over others, transformational leaders can work to win the commitment of peers, colleagues, partners, allies, and more senior managers, through inspiration and persuasion. Leaders are needed at all levels of an organisation, not only to be active within their sphere of responsibility, leading their own teams, but also to be proactive in seeking support to bring about changes that require the cooperation of colleagues, or the approval of more senior figures.

Establishing direction, through developing and communicating a shared vision, is a key element of this type of leadership. As Peter Senge (1990) says: 'In a corporation, a shared vision changes people's relationship with the company. It is no longer "their company"; it becomes "our company".'

A shared vision provides clarity, a focus for energy, and a set of guiding principles for action. The need for a leader to create a vision might apply equally whether they are a chief executive of a Trust, a head of a directorate, the leader of a team, or simply someone trying to establish a coalition of like-minded individuals working across organisational boundaries.

The process of developing such a vision is by no means a mystical quest or an exercise in individual imagination. Successful visions of the future are grounded in the reality of the present. Leaders must be prepared to work hard to gather and assess information about the organisation, and develop insight into what key stakeholders want. Good leaders must be good listeners, and good observers of what is around them, in order to develop visions that will win commitment to change.

To achieve a *shared* vision requires communication – leaders need to be able to set out the vision in clear and compelling ways, consistently and persistently, to win commitment. This communication takes place through both words and deeds, and is greatly enhanced by forming good relationships with others based on genuine concern for their well-being (Alimo-Metcalfe and Alban-Metcalfe 2000).

Successful leadership, therefore, necessarily entails innovation and change. It involves determining direction, engaging commitment, unlocking the power to innovate, and supporting team members and colleagues through change.

These dimensions of leadership explain, to a large extent, the interests of some of the contributors to this book in understanding the values, beliefs and motivations of fellow managers and professionals in the health service, for these form the frameworks which can either support effective leadership, or prevent it from taking place. Other contributors have focused on leadership processes – exploring how innovation and change can best be brought about – or the skills that are necessary for successful leadership in the complex network of organisations and professions that is the modern NHS.

Leading innovation and change in the NHS in the twenty-first century is by no means an easy task, but it is part of the job description of every health service manager and responsible clinician.

The chapters that follow illustrate some of the current concerns of managers and professionals in the health service. How to achieve effective leadership across health care organisations? How best to work in partnership? How to engage clinicians at all levels in management? How to achieve clinical governance? How to create the new organisations that are required to develop the 21st century health service?

References

Alimo-Metcalfe, B., and Alban-Metcalfe, R. (2000) 'Heaven can wait' *Health Service Journal* 12 October pp 26–29

Bennis W., and Nanus, B. (1985 &1997) *Leaders: the Strategies for Taking Charge* New York: Harper & Row, 2nd ed Harper Business

de Bono, E. (1978) *Lateral Thinking* London: Penguin

DoH (1997) *The New NHS: modern, dependable* Cm 3807

DoH (1998) *A First Class Service: Quality in the NHS*

DoH (2000) *The NHS Plan* Cm 4818

Griffiths Report (1983) 'The NHS Management Inquiry' London: DHSS

Hamel, G. and Prahalad, C.K. (1994) *Competing for the Future* Boston: Harvard Business School Press

Hamel, G. (2000) *Leading the Revolution*, Boston: Harvard Business School Press

Harrison, S., and Pollitt, C. (1994) *Controlling Health Professionals*, Buckingham: Open University Press

Kotter, J. (1990) *A Force for Change* New York: The Free Press

MacGregor Burns, J. (1978) *Leadership* New York: Harper and Row

Mintzberg, H. and Waters, J.A. (1985) 'Of strategies, deliberate and emergent' *Strategic Management Journal* vol 6 no 3

Peters, T. J., and Waterman, R.H., (1982) *In Search of Excellence* New York: Harper and Row

Porter, M. (1996) 'What is strategy?' *Harvard Business Review*, Nov–Dec

Secretary of State (2000) Alan Milburn 'A Health Service of All the Talents' Human Resources in the NHS Conference, Birmingham, February 28

Senge, P. 1990 *The Fifth Discipline: The art and practice of the learning organisation* New York: Doubleday

White, R.P., Hodgson, P. and Crainer, S. (1996) *The Future of Leadership*, London, Pitman

Zaleznik, A. (1977) 'Managers and Leaders: Are They Different ?' *Harvard Business Review* May/June pp 67–78

CHAPTER TWO

Strategic Health Authorities – competent for the future?

Carole Langrick

Introduction

At the time of writing, in mid-2001, the NHS is about to embark on what is probably the most significant change of its structure since the 1974 reorganisation. Usually change in the NHS involves one or two structural tiers at a time in a cyclical pattern. This time there is major change taking place throughout all the structural elements at the same time:

- Regional Offices of the NHS Executive will be replaced by a Regional Director of Health and Social Care with a small group of supporting staff.
- Health Authorities will be merged to reduce the number by two thirds resulting in 30 or so. They will absorb the performance management functions of Regional Offices. It is likely that they will retain the responsibility for strategic leadership for a larger area.
- All Primary Care Groups will complete the transition to Primary Care Trusts and assume greater responsibilities.
- NHS Trusts will become accountable to the new Strategic Health Authorities and some will be transferring services to Primary Care Trusts.

For Health Authorities, this change in their structure and role is probably not surprising and could be said to be long overdue. Since the early 1990's there has been continuing uncertainty in parts of the NHS as to exactly the purpose and function of Health Authorities (Jarrold, 1999). *Leadership for Health* (DoH, 1990) tried to define the role of Health

Authorities in a modern health service but it is debatable how many of the existing organisations have risen to the challenge of providing strategic leadership to the local health system.

So why do we think that the new Strategic Health Authorities will rise to the challenge that their predecessors were unable to meet?

For any organisation to be an effective strategic leader, not least a Health Authority or a new Strategic Health Authority, there are two prerequisites. Firstly, there must be a clear definition and understanding of what is meant by 'strategic leadership'. Secondly, the organisation must possess the competencies that will be required of a strategic leader.

My research was conducted in early 2000 with the aims of:

1. Defining strategic leadership.
2. Identifying the competencies required by Health Authorities to be strategic leaders.

It was focused on Health Authorities because Strategic Health Authorities, had not become a firm policy direction at the time. However, the outcomes of the research are eminently applicable to Strategic Health Authorities if they are to be the next generation of strategic leaders.

Methodology

The approach had four distinct stages. Firstly, analysis of government publications to assess direction, if any, being given by the Department of Health regarding the role of Health Authorities and the competencies required. Secondly, a literature search to understand current theory on strategic leadership and competencies. Thirdly, semi-structured interviews to elicit qualitative data and, fourthly, questionnaires to a wider sample to test and verify the results of the interviews.

In respect of the interviews, the semi-structured approach was chosen to allow exploration of themes and real events from the subjects' experiences. The themes covered were:

• The interviewee's understanding of 'strategic leadership'
• Critical incidents or events from the interviewee's experience which typify the subject's definition of 'strategic leadership'

- The interviewee's assessment of the competencies required by a Health Authority to be a strategic leader.

Eleven interviews were completed. The sample consisted of 4 Health Authority Chief Executives (one Deputy included in this sample), 4 NHS Trust Chief Executives and 3 Primary Care Group Chairs.

The outcomes of the interviews in relation to competencies were tested and verified using a questionnaire. From the 29 competencies identified in the interviews, respondents were asked to identify the 5 most important and the 5 least important competencies. The questionnaire was designed in this way to identify threshold and differentiating competencies. Threshold competencies are the essential characteristics needed to be minimally effective. Differentiating competencies are those factors that distinguish superior from average performance (Spencer and Spencer, 1993).

140 questionnaires were posted to a randomly selected sample and 51 were returned giving a response rate of 36%. This was made up of:

- 11 Health Authority Chief Executives (37% response rate)
- 24 NHS Trust Chief Executives (43% response rate)
- 16 Primary Care Group Chief Executives (30% response rate).

The 'chi-squared' statistical method was used to ascertain the statistical significance of the responses at a 95% confidence level.

Findings

Figure 1 summarises the findings of the study. It shows that the key purpose of the Health Authority is to provide strategic leadership (DoH, 1999). It defines strategic leadership according to five key roles. It also shows the 29 competencies, identified via the interviews, required by Health Authorities in order to fulfil these five roles. Of the 29, seven are differentiating competencies, that is, they have been chosen by the respondents to the questionnaire as 'most important' and application of the 'chi-squared' test reveals the frequency of choosing to be statistically significant at a 95% confidence interval. Differentiating competencies are those factors that distinguish superior from average performance.

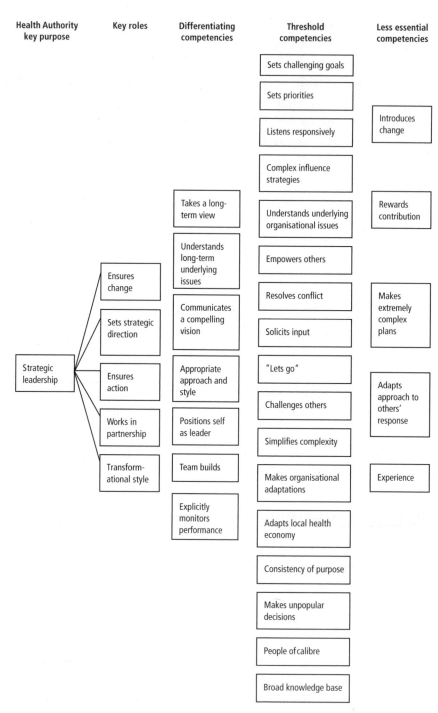

Figure 1: Summary of research findings

Seventeen can be deemed to be threshold competencies in that respondents to the questionnaire chose them as neither most or least important. Threshold competencies are the essential competencies that all Health Authorities will need in order to be minimally effective. Five competencies were chosen by the questionnaire respondents as 'least important' and application of the 'chi-squared' test reveals the frequency of choosing to be statistically significant at a 95% confidence interval.

Strategic leadership

Five strategic leadership roles were identified from the literature search and confirmed by the interviews:

- Ensures the Introduction of Change of Enduring Value
- Sets Strategic Direction
- Ensures Action
- Promotes and Works in Partnership
- Transformational Style – has vision and encourages ownership and empowerment

There was a high level of consistency across the interviews in terms of these roles being identified. The interview method encouraged interviewees to identify the various aspects rather than concentrating on a single, narrow definition of 'strategic leadership'. Six interviewees identified four roles, with the remaining five highlighting all five. Figure 2 shows the frequency of identification of each of the roles in the interviews.

Transformational style was identified by all interviewees as an important role. This was followed by setting strategic direction and partnership working as next important. Ensuring the introduction of change and ensuring action were identified by nine of the interviewees.

Competencies

Boyatzis (1982) defines competencies as underlying characteristics in that they may be motives, traits, skills or bodies of knowledge that are causally related to effective or superior performance in a job. It is the causal relationship between possessing the competencies and the link to effective

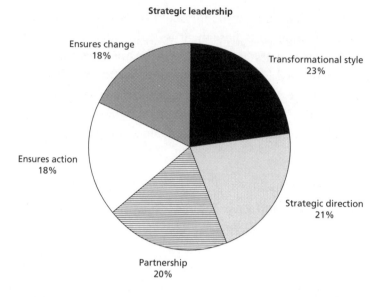

Strategic leadership

Figure 2: Diagram to show the frequency with which each of the strategic leadership roles of Health Authorities were identified by interviewees

performance that is important. Boyatzis (1982) uses the model in Figure 3 to explain the relationship between competencies and job performance.

According to this model, an effective Health Authority will have the required competencies for strategic leadership that match the requirements of the job and the environment in which it operates. Effective performance will only occur when all three critical components of the model are consistent or 'fit'.

There are two distinct approaches to identifying competencies. The behavioural approach identifies them as a number of behavioural indicators that define the competency in action. The alternative approach is the output model which is primarily concerned with deciding the outcomes that are to be achieved. This research followed a behavioural approach.

Perhaps the most comprehensive of the behavioural competency models is the generic competency dictionary developed by the McBer Consultancy, which is based on several hundred research studies conducted over a 20 year period (Spencer and Spencer 1993).

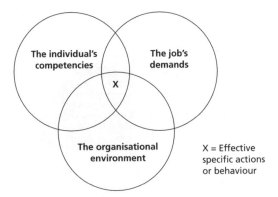

Figure 3: A model of effective job performance showing the inter-relationship between competencies, job demands and the environment (from Boyatzis, 1982)

Analysing the interviews using the McBer competencies resulted in 24 competencies being identified. In addition, five 'new' competencies not previously included in the generic competency dictionary were identified:

- **Consistency of Purpose** – Sticks to pursuing the same key objectives over the long term – while it remains relevant to do so.
- **People of Calibre** – Sufficient people with the appropriate skills, attitudes and behaviours to provide and support the strategic leadership role. (It is arguable as to whether this is a contextual factor or whether it is a competency.)
- **Appropriate Approach and Style** – Realistic and pragmatic; persuasive and convincing; energy, drive, enthusiasm and commitment; persistence and determination – does not give up easily when things are not going smoothly; behaves with integrity – demonstrating honesty, openness and genuineness; inclusive.
- **Experience** – Expertise and track record of dealing successfully with complex health care issues.
- **Broad Knowledge Base** – Wide breadth and depth of knowledge and understanding of health care issues and services.

The full list of 29 competencies required by Health Authorities to be Strategic Leaders as identified are presented in Table 1.

Table 1: Competencies required by Health Authorities to be strategic leaders

Competency		Description	Source
Achievement orientation	Sets challenging goals	Sets and acts to reach challenging goals for the local health economy	Modified S&S
Achievement orientation	Introduces change and transformation	Does new things that change and transform either some or all of the structures, systems and processes within the local health economy	Modified S&S
Achievement orientation	Sets priorities	Makes decisions and sets priorities on the basis of cost-benefit analysis	Modified S&S
Initiative	Takes a long-term view	Anticipates situations 5–10 years ahead and acts to create opportunities or avoid problems.	Modified S&S
Interpersonal understanding	Listens responsively	Actively listens to people and ensures that all the different views are taken into account.	Modified S&S
Impact and influence	Complex influence strategies	Uses a variety of approaches to influence others, tailored to individual situations.	Modified S&S
Organisational awareness	Understands long-term underlying issues	Understands and interprets the implications of long-term underlying problems, opportunities or political forces affecting the local health economy in relation to the external world.	Modified S&S
Organisational awareness	Understands underlying organisational issues	Understands (and addresses) the reasons for ongoing organisational behaviour within, and affecting, the local health economy	Modified S&S
Teamwork and co-operation	Team builds	Acts to develop and maintain a shared vision and direction by the ongoing inclusion and involvement of all members of the local health economy.	Modified S&S
Teamwork and co-operation	Empowers others	Encourages and enables others.	Modified S&S
Teamwork and co-operation	Resolves conflict	Brings conflict within the local health economy into the open and encourages or facilitates a beneficial resolution.	S&S
Teamwork and co-operation	Solicits input	Genuinely values other's input and expertise. Encourages ideas and opinions to help form specific decisions or plans.	Modified S&S
Team leadership	Communicates a compelling vision	Communicates a compelling vision, which generates enthusiasm and commitment in the local health economy.	Modified S&S
Team leadership	Positions self as leader	Has clear understanding of the roles and responsibilities of the strategic leadership role and ensures 'buy-in' of others within the local health economy and exercises clear leadership of key issues.	Substantially modified S&S
Developing others	'Lets go'	Is 'tight' on the delivery of agreed outcomes and 'loose' on the means by which they are achieved	Substantially modified S&S

(continued)

Table 1: Competencies required by Health Authorities to be strategic leaders
(continued)

Competency		Description	Source
Developing others	Rewards contribution	Recognises and rewards contributions of members of the local health economy	Substantially modified S&S
Directiveness	Challenges others	Challenges others openly and directly to encourage innovative thinking or to expose underlying blockages to progress	Substantially modified S&S
Directiveness	Explicitly monitors performance	Explicitly holds the local health economy to account against clear standards	Modified S&S
Analytical thinking	Makes extremely complex plans or analyses	Organises, sequences and analyses extremely complex interdependent systems	S&S
Conceptual thinking	Simplifies complexity	Pulls together ideas, issues and observations into a single concept or a clear presentation. Identifies a key issue in a complex situation.	S&S
Flexibility	Adapts approach to situation or to other's response	Changes behaviour or approach to suit the situation	Modified S&S
Flexibility	Makes organisational adaptations	Makes adaptations in own organisation in response to the needs of the situation	Modified S&S
Flexibility	Adapts local health economy	Initiates large, long term or significant adaptations in the local health economy in response to the needs of the situation.	Substantially modified S&S
Organisational commitment	Makes unpopular decisions	Is prepared to take and stand by decisions that benefit the greater local health economy and their patients even when they are unpopular or controversial	Substantially modified S&S
Consistency of purpose	Consistency of purpose	Sticks to pursuing the same key objectives over the long term – whilstever they remain relevant. Does what they say they are going to do.	New
People of calibre	People of calibre	Sufficient people with the appropriate skills, attitudes and behaviours to provide and support the strategic leadership role.	New
Attitudes and values	Appropriate approach and style	Realistic and pragmatic; Persuasive and convincing; Energy, drive, enthusiasm and commitment; Persistence and determination – does not give up easily when things are not going smoothly; behaves with integrity – demonstrating honesty, openness and genuineness; Inclusive.	New
Accumulated experience	Experience	Expertise and track record of dealing successfully with complex health and health care issues.	New
Broad knowledge base	Broad knowledge base	Wide breadth and depth of knowledge and understanding of health and health care issues and services. Possess functional knowledge and expertise (e.g. finance, public health) and is able to access detailed specialist expertise as required.	New

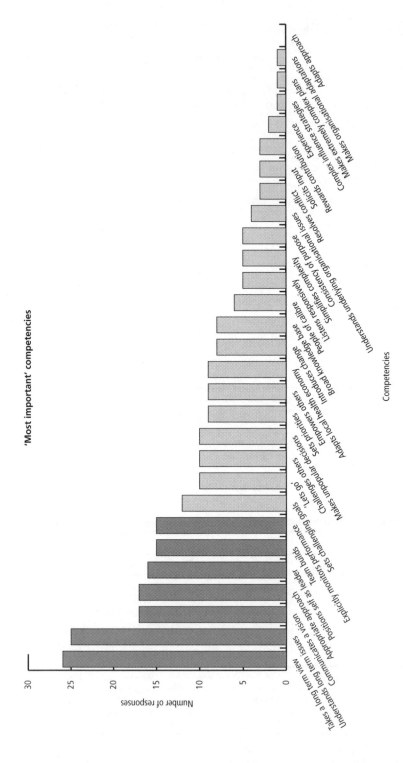

Figure 4: Graph to show the ranking of the competencies according to the 'most important' for a Health Authority to have to be a strategic leader

When asked to indicate the 'most important' competencies, the ensuing ranking, based on the number of responses per competency, is shown in Figure 4.

Application of the 'chi-squared' statistical test revealed that the top seven are statistically significant at the 95% confidence interval. That is:

- Takes a long term view
- Understands long term underlying issues
- Communicates a compelling vision
- Appropriate approach and style
- Positions self as leader
- Team builds
- Explicitly monitors performance

These competencies could be thought of as differentiating competencies – they distinguish superior from average performance. On this basis, these competencies are essential to effective strategic leadership.

When asked to indicate the 'least important' competencies, the ensuing ranking is shown in Figure 5 overleaf.

Application of the 'chi-squared' statistical test revealed that the top five are statistically significant at the 95% confidence interval. That is:

- Makes extremely complex plans and analyses
- Rewards contribution
- Introduces change
- Adapts approach to suit situation or others' response
- Experience.

These five competencies are seen as least essential.

The competencies that remain after the most and least important have been identified can be thought of as representing the threshold competencies required by Health Authorities to be strategic leaders. Threshold competencies are the essential characteristics that all Health Authorities will need in order to fulfil the role to the minimum required level. The threshold competencies therefore are:

- Sets challenging goals
- 'Lets go'

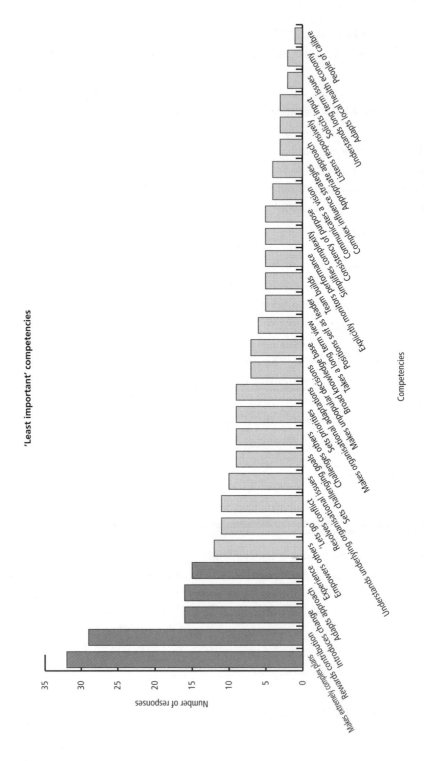

Figure 5: Graph to show the 'least important' competencies identified by the questionnaire respondents

- Challenges others
- Makes unpopular decisions
- Sets priorities
- Empowers others
- Adapts local health economy
- Broad knowledge base
- Right people
- Listens responsively
- Simplifies complexity
- Consistency of purpose
- Understands underlying organisational issues
- Resolves conflict
- Solicits input
- Complex influence strategies
- Makes organisational adaptations.

Implications for the new Strategic Health Authorities

This study set out to interpret the strategic leadership requirement in practical terms by:

1. Defining strategic leadership
2. Identifying the competencies that Health Authorities will need to be strategic leaders.

Strategic leadership

The literature search had identified that 'strategic leadership' is a multi-faceted concept that is better understood by breaking it down into its key elements or roles. Five roles were identified and these were consistently raised in the interviews:

- Ensures the introduction of change of enduring value
- Sets strategic direction
- Ensures action
- Promotes and works in partnership
- Transformational style.

However, there was a tendency for people to use the words 'strategic leadership' in a generic sense as though it were a one dimensional role with a single meaning that is understood by all. That this is the case, perhaps accounts for some of the continuing uncertainty within certain parts of the NHS about the role of Health Authorities (Jarrold, 1999). It was only by exploring examples that the various facets of the role became apparent. Thus, a Health Authority can be said to be a strategic leader when it is setting strategic direction. Alternatively, it can be said to be a strategic leader when it is ensuring change of a long-term nature takes place within the local health system or when it is working in partnership with other organisations on issues of longer-term importance. If confusion and resentment are to be avoided then the emphasis needs to move towards being more specific about the breadth and multi-faceted nature of strategic leadership. Identification of the five facets is the beginning of this process but the discussion and shared understanding needs to be developed within each health 'family'.

Competencies

Boyatzis (1982) emphasised the link between competencies, the demands of the job and the environment for effective performance. An effective Strategic Health Authority will have the required competencies for strategic leadership that match the requirements of the job and the environment in which it operates. This study has identified the requirements of the job in terms of the five strategic leadership roles listed previously.

In line with Boyatzis' (1982) model and against this backdrop of job demands and environment, this study has identified 29 competencies required by Health Authorities. This approach of trying to identify organisational competencies has been relatively novel given the paucity of published work on this area. The comprehensive work published by Spencer and Spencer (1993) and others on individual competencies has provided a useful framework to which respondents could relate. Because organisations are made up of a large number of individuals, however, this study has not been able to identify the location within the organisation of particular competencies, but it is probably safe to assume that the differentiating competencies and threshold competencies will need to be widely held by top and middle managers. The actual balance of competencies required by each individual manager would be dependent on the role they are fulfilling and would need to be identified within the context of the competencies required by the Strategic Health Authority in which they work.

Hamel and Prahalad (1994), whilst not detracting from the need to acquire or develop competencies at the level of the individual within organisations, suggest that top managers should view the firm as a portfolio of competencies. It is the amalgamation of all the competencies at whatever place or position within the organisation that guarantees whether the organisation is successful. This view would seem to fit with the approach taken by this study inasmuch as the intention has been to identify this overall portfolio.

Seven competencies were identified as 'most important':

- Takes a long term view
- Understands long term underlying issues
- Communicates a compelling vision
- Appropriate approach and style
- Positions self as leader
- Team builds
- Explicitly monitors performance.

It seems reasonable to assume that all Strategic Health Authorities will need to possess these competencies.

Seventeen competencies were deemed to be neither 'most' nor 'least' important. On this basis it seems reasonable to categorise these as threshold competencies and required by all Strategic Health Authorities as a minimum.

Hamel and Prahalad (1994) use the phrase 'strategic architecture' to describe the broad competencies that an organisation has to build to take it into the future. They see this strategic architecture as a map. This study has provided Strategic Health Authorities with a map of the competencies required for strategic leadership. The next step for any Strategic Health Authority taking this forward would be to undertake a competency gap analysis and then devise an Organisational Development Programme to address any deficits.

References

Boyatzis, R.E. (1982) *The Competent Manager: A Model for Effective Performance.* New York: John Wiley & Sons.

Department of Health (1999) *Leadership For Health: The Health Authority Role.* London: The Stationary Office Limited.

Hamel, G. & Prahalad, C.K. (1994) *Competing for the Future.* Boston: Harvard Business School Press.

Jarrold, K. (1999) 'Pulling Together'. *Health Management.* 3(9), pp. 16–17.

Spencer, L.M. Jnr. and Spencer, S.M. (1993) *Competence at Work: Models for Superior Performance.* Toronto, Canada: John Wiley & Sons Inc.

■ Carole Langrick is Director of Health Systems Performance at Tees Health Authority

CHAPTER THREE

The scars on my back – exploring leadership in a changing NHS

Ian Cameron

Introduction

Leading change in the National Health Service is not easy. Just ask the Prime Minister, Tony Blair, who admitted to an audience of entrepreneurs in July 1999, 'You try getting change in the public sector and public services. I bear the scars on my back after two years in government' (cited in Rawnsley, 2001). At the time, the government was setting up 'the most dramatic experiment in the history of the NHS' with the creation of Primary Care Groups and Trusts (Dixon and Sweeney, 2001). It seems though, to have been ever thus. For example, the changes that brought in the internal market in 1991 were considered the most radical reorganisation of the health service since its inception in 1948 (Robinson, 1996).

As a Consultant in Public Health Medicine with Leeds Health Authority, I am expected to be effective 'in a multi-professional, multi-agency environment and be able to achieve multi-sectoral change' (Alderslade and Hunter, 1992, p23). This requires knowledge about current national, and local, organisational policy. In 1997, I wanted to increase my understanding about the recently introduced national policy of a Primary Care Led NHS and also what impact this would have on the leadership role of the Health Authority.

To do this, I interviewed staff from Leeds Health Authority and Leeds general practitioners, using the work of Glaser and Strauss (1967) as the basis of a qualitative research methodology. Then, using key components of leadership as derived from the literature, plus readings on a primary care led NHS, recommendations were made on how the Health Authority should take forward a leadership role. The findings from this research can now be compared with the current changes to make the NHS modern and dependable (Department of Health, 2001).

A primary care led NHS

Working for Patients (Secretaries of State, 1989) heralded, on 1st April 1991, the creation of the purchaser-provider split or the internal market. Health Authorities purchased services, while NHS Trusts provided them. In addition, GP Fundholders became a further purchaser, albeit on a limited basis, but by 1996, options had been expanded with community fundholding, standard fundholding, total purchasing (NHS Executive, 1994). Two subsequent White Papers on primary care promoted salaried general practitioners and practice based contracts (Department of Health, 1996a, 1996b).

The term a 'primary care led NHS' had by now been introduced (NHS Executive, 1994). The only meaning offered for the term was that, 'decisions about the purchasing and providing of health care are taken as close to patients as possible' (NHS Executive, 1994). For Meads (1996, p1) it was clear that this meant, 'Primary Care will lead the management and development of the NHS'. However, although the phrase may have been 'rapidly absorbed into NHS management speak' (Liddell, 1996, p1), a Director at the NHS Executive admitted that 'it is an often used phrase, (but) there is a great deal less certainty about its meaning' (McKeon, 1996, p237). Despite this, there was recognition that all these changes 'could alter British primary care profoundly' (Groves, 1997) and that their potential impact 'should not be underestimated' (Meads and Wilkin, 1994, p6). In this context of a primary care led NHS, Health Authorities were now to focus less on purchasing and more on providing support to general practices, both as providers and purchasers. (Colin-Thome, 1996)

Methodology

A qualitative approach was considered best suited to understanding people's attitudes and behaviour towards a primary care led NHS. The grounded theory approach by Glaser and Strauss (1967) is concerned with generating theory from data systematically obtained and analysed, through constant comparative analysis. This seemed a particularly appropriate approach as 'the strongest case for the use of grounded theory is in investigations of relatively uncharted waters' (Stern, 1980, p2).

Interviews were used rather than questionnaires in order to 'produce a very rich body of data expressed in the respondents' own words and context' (Hammersley and Atkinson, 1995). The recruitment of participants was based on the desire 'to maximise the probability of the desired outcome'. (Stewart and Shamdasini, 1990, p53). The criteria for selection were that Health Authority staff should have a significant knowledge about primary care, and have responsibility in this area. General practitioners were selected on the basis of involvement in recent developments on the primary care agenda, and having significant knowledge and experience of the ways and workings of the Health Authority.

The six interviews included directors in primary and community care, a first wave GP fundholder and a community fundholder. Each were interviewed for half an hour and each interview began with the same broad open ended question. From then on, the interview was unstructured, in order to 'allow respondents a great deal of freedom to provide the amount of information they want to give' (Stewart and Shamdasani, 1990, p74).

The full transcripts were worked through and divided into meaning units or 'a descriptive phrase, sentence or series of sentences which convey one idea or one related set of perceptions' (Mostyn cited by Burnard, 1994). A continuous process of comparison was undertaken with the aim that a 'category system should emerge or the data should offer a clear or true representation of the things that were talked about in the interview' (Burnard, 1994, p22).

Results

From the wealth of data from the interviews, six main categories emerged with a range of sub-categories that are illustrated with quotes in the boxes below. The first category covered where Leeds was coming from (Box 1). This can be summarised as 'I think historically there is a feeling that Leeds has been behind, as it were, leading innovation over the last few years'. The reasons fell on three players – Leeds Health Authority, general practitioners and the Acute Trusts.

Box 1: The historical position

■ **Health Authority**
"in the past we have not been able to be the leaders locally"
"primary care is foreign to them"

■ **Primary Care**
"no obvious striking locality voices"
"bogged down with the workload"

■ **Acute Trusts**
"have dictated.........the Health Authority's agenda for far too long"

Box 2: Change in Leeds

■ **Health Authority**
"Facing up to the Acute Trust at last"

■ **Primary Care**
"able to take a stand"

There was, though, a feeling of positive change (Box 2). A new Chief Executive at the Health Authority with an interest in primary care had made 'a huge difference'. The overall message was Leeds is 'catching up', but recognition that 'we've still got a long way to go'.

Much was said about a 'primary care led NHS' (Box 3), including how unhelpful the term was, being vague and 'coming from a political need'. One interviewee strongly preferred the term 'a primary care *informed* NHS'. A consistent message that emerged was around the need for 'balance' involving primary care, the Trusts, the Health Authority, service users and carers. More specifically, a change in the power relationship with the Acute Trust to enable 'a re-design, to reconfigure the health services everywhere'.

In terms of leadership, general practitioners were clear about the role of the Health Authority – 'it is the Health Authority's responsibility to be leaders in health services', 'leadership… is clearly a job of management'. In contrast, Health Authority staff had the most doubts about their role

---

Box 3: A primary care led NHS

■ **Definition**
"a handy piece of rhetoric and it means anything to anybody really"
"everyone comes at it from a different angle"

■ **Features**
"wherever it is possible to do things on a local basis with community staff"
"primary care more and more involved, driving agendas, setting them"
"talking more across divides"

■ **Changing context**
"it will become increasingly impractical for fundholders to work in isolation"
"(The White Papers)....... have been like a depth charge thrown into it"

Box 4: Roles of the Health Authority

■ **Promotion of primary care**
"making primary care professionals more involved in commissioning and making provision more primary care led"

■ **Strategy**
"enabling primary care to be something coherent when primary care is so disparate"

■ **Managing relationships**
"holding the ring on these whole system issues"

■ **Equity**
"looking at populations, rather than individuals"

■ **Performance management**
"a little bit like a policeman's role"

■ **Keeping the debate open**
"keep open our minds and other people's minds"

---

in a primary care led NHS – 'you begin to say what is the role of the Health Authority in that setting?', 'what is the Health Authority's leading role?' A number of roles did emerge (Box 4).

Box 5: Tasks for the Health Authority

■ **Building up relationships with primary care**
"sophisticated networking is required"

■ **Education of Health Authority staff about primary care**
"Health Authority should be staffed with primary care voices"

■ **Develop appropriate structures and systems**
"have you got the right people sitting around the table with the Health Authority bringing the views from the localities"

■ **Develop primary care**
"get practices working together, the better ones will raise the standards of the less developed ones"

■ **Develop levers**
"Health Authority needs to make movement advantageous"

To progress the roles, five significant tasks emerged for the Health Authority (Box 5). These included building relationships with primary care; educating Health Authority staff about primary care; enhancing structures and systems through locality commissioning, liaison arrangements with practices, increased general practitioner involvement; developing the skills of primary care staff and the organisation of practices and between practices; developing levers to ensure change and progress, including the use of resources. However, it was clear that the Health Authority faced a number of significant problems (Box 6).

These problems included the Health Authority's own history; the lack of knowledge about primary care which 'would take a long time to rectify'; handling the increasing conflicts of interest; tackling the accountability issue specifically over finance and general practitioners. The final problem was considered to be a lack of medical leadership at the Health Authority, general practice and the Trusts.

Discussion

Leadership can be defined as, 'the influencing of assumptions, beliefs, values, norms or behaviour, of other group members in an intended

Box 6: Problems faced by the health authority

■ **Own history**
"the problem is we are not starting with a blank sheet"

■ **Lack of knowledge**
"I think a lot of people are scared to admit how little they know"

■ **Handling conflicts of interest**
"primary care are the commissioners but also the provides, that's the difficulties we are going to run into"

■ **Lack of accountability**
"the more devolved it gets, the less control you have and the less levers you have"

■ **Lack of medical leadership**
"(Do general practitioners) have the skills, commitments, strategic vision to be able to lead disparate practices?"

direction' (adapted from Wright, 1996). Drawing on just some of the vast literature on leadership, four key features emerge – creating a vision; developing followers; establishing and managing the change agenda; reflection and self-learning (Management Research Group Gmbh, 1992; Wright, 1996; Kotter, 1995; Garratt, 1990). These four elements were used along with the literature on primary care and the categories previously described as the basis on which to consider further the leadership role of Leeds Health Authority in developing a primary care led NHS.

The first step to fulfilling that role must be that 'you've got to want to be in charge' (Roberts, 1989, p23). Leeds Health Authority, however, expressed reservations whether this was an appropriate role for the Health Authority to take. This is in the context of a Health Authority dominated by a secondary care perspective, a lack of knowledge of primary care and a lot of caveats about the notion of a primary care led NHS.

In terms of creating a vision or 'the picture that drives all the action' (Belasco, 1990, p11) the interviewees clearly saw a much greater influence by primary care, and a more even power relationship with the Acute Trusts. However, the comment that 'we are being so cautious' is supported by the views that strategy would emerge, purchasing would be within the framework of the Health Authority and that Health Maintenance Organisations were the 'extreme' end of the spectrum. By contrast, across the country there were examples of bolder, more innovative practice and thinking. For example, there was a multi-practice and community trust consortium (Coulter and Mays, 1997), and a limited company set up by general practitioners (Robinson, 1996). Future options being discussed included health authorities commissioning a comprehensive package of primary care services from a single provider organisation (Meads and Wilkin, 1997); one stop primary care combined with one stop shopping (Groves, 1997); Health Maintenance Organisations (Cresswell, 1997); primary care organisations managed by trusts or consortia of general practitioners (Pringle, 1997); integrated care between staff from primary care, community health, social services, secondary care (Ham, 1997) and locally determined contracts with organisations rather than national contracts with individual general practitioners (Pringle, 1997).

Mobilising support for a vision is often stated in terms of involving and empowering staff within, and across, an organisation in creating and sharing that vision (Hinterhuber and Popp, 1992). For the Health Authority this involves a complex multi-agency system, including the 'semi-autonomous businesses' that make up general practice. Having credibility with clinical practitioners is seen as crucial for successful joint working (Hill and Shepherd, 1997). On that basis then it was well recognised by the interviewees that a lot of work was needed, in Leeds, with general practices to establish the type of relationship necessary for this to come about.

Establishing and managing the change agenda requires leaders to, 'act and get others, to act to empower (their) own vision' (Belasco, 1990, p127). In terms of the health service Stewart (1996) believes a key leadership task is to 'enlist doctors co-operation in the provision of effective and efficient health care'. While this was recognised by interviewees, the levels of leadership actually available from doctors in Leeds came in for critical comment. Despite reassurances from the NHS Executive (1996b) that primary care is more than just general practitioners, it was clear that there was concern that the future will be a GP led medical model, excluding other primary care staff, in particular nursing (Pearson, 1996; Salter and Snee, 1997). This had been the experience of one interviewee, who had to constantly say to general practitioners, 'Right, this is a medical model at the minute ... what about a pharmacy input, what about a nursing input, what about a dental input?'

Creating systems and structures, with appropriate resources and delegation, is crucial to the change agenda (Kotter, 1995). However, although locality commissioning was seen as the way forward by the Health Authority, there was the comment that, 'we're a long way from devolving budgets'.

Handling obstacles, whether political, analytical or educational, is also a significant element of managing the change agenda (Pettigrew and Whipp, 1991). There was acceptance that the Health Authority had a leadership role in, 'managing differential power relationships', in what was also seen as an increasingly complex system. Being able to monitor and review progress is key (Belasco, 1990). While this was recognised as important, especially over finance, there were highly critical comments about current accountability arrangements, with a feeling that general practice had 'got away with it at the moment', and that the accountability framework for GP fundholders (Department of Health, 1994) was, 'if not bordering on the farce, not far from it'.

The final key feature of leadership considered is around reflection and self-learning. The primary care led NHS was new territory and the issues, 'reach to the heart of the NHS as we have known it' (Meads and Wilkin, 1997, p6). Interviewees stressed the need to keep the debate open and to learn from the mistakes from others, because as one put it, 'nobody has all the answers, and nobody knows all the issues about primary care'.

Recommendations

Drawing the themes of leadership and a primary care led NHS together, the following recommendations could be made to the Health Authority. The Health Authority must:

- acknowledge it has a leadership role and ensure this is effective;
- accept that the future shape of a primary care led NHS will be radical and far reaching;
- develop that vision for the future from the grass roots, involving general practitioners, others in primary care, secondary care, services users and carers;

- develop strong working relationships with general practice;
- demonstrate commitment by tackling those areas of immediate concern to general practitioners;
- ensure nursing, pharmacy and therapy services are involved in commissioning and decision-making alongside general practitioners;
- systematically develop appropriate management skills for general practitioners;
- ensure its internal structures and systems support the primary care agenda;
- develop robust monitoring and review arrangements, including practice based benchmarking of financial, process and outcome indicators;
- seek to maintain and build on existing good primary care practice within Leeds;
- ensure that a primary led NHS reduces the health inequalities in Leeds and not exacerbates them;
- facilitate further debate and discussion across interested parties in the future of a primary care led NHS in Leeds.

Reflections

At the time of carrying out this research, I commented that there were major similarities to the findings by Kotter (1995) on successful change in the private sector. Kotter too was talking about major change, 'transformation (that) is impossible unless hundreds or thousands of people are willing to help *within* (my emphasis) an organisation' (1995, p63). The transformation change required in Leeds for a primary care led NHS however was occurring not within a single organisation, but rather with independent contractor general practitioners, NHS Trusts, the Local Authority, the voluntary sector, the private sector, notwithstanding the Department of Health, service users and carers and numerous other competing agendas. The proposed recommendations therefore had to be recognised as having a complexity and a challenge quite additional to that found in the commercial sector. The need was for transformational leadership (Bass and Avolio, 1993) or 'Leadership and performance beyond expectations' (Sashkin and Rosenbach, 1993, p89).

In the event, a Labour government came into power in May 1997. Quickly, the government removed the internal market and fundholding and set out its own vision for the National Health Service which included putting primary and community services at its heart (Department of Health, 1997). In contrast to the ill-defined primary care led NHS, this was a national vision supported by a variety of plans, statutory duties and National Service Frameworks (Department of Health 19978, 1998a,b,c, 2000a,b, 2001b). These were a requirement not an option for Leeds or elsewhere. To help provide ownership, national, regional and local champions were established alongside czars and a host of other initiatives. The need for appropriate systems and structures for delivery was recognised. New statutory organisations, Primary Care Groups and Trusts were established (NHS Executive, 1999). A number of local obstacles and concerns identified by the Leeds interviewees around a primary care led NHS would therefore be removed by these developments. Crucially though, and supporting the perceived adverse impact of the history of Leeds Health Authority on being able to implement change, the government also proposed the abolition of Health Authorities (Department of Health, 2001a). In other words, Health Authorities were not the leadership solution, but rather part of the problem.

However, the Department of Health has had to do a lot of self-learning. The Leeds' interviewees recognised that it would be local people who have to have the leadership skills to drive and sustain the change agenda. Altering systems and structures is not enough. Rather belatedly, this has now been recognised nationally with the publication of Shifting the Power (Department of Health, 2001a). Significantly, the subtitle is Securing Delivery. A national leadership programme is to be established backed up by a recent major survey of NHS managers that has helped define the transformational style of leadership that is now required (Alimo-Metcalfe and Alban-Metcalfe, 2000).

The current changes do present major challenges, and although there is now less talk of a primary care led NHS (Higgins, 2001) there will undoubtedly be equally significant changes in the future. Whatever emerges will need leadership and this will require articulation of a clear vision that has local support but will equally require actions to ensure successful implementation on the ground. If these lessons can be absorbed then perhaps, just perhaps, there will be fewer scars developing on the backs of the Prime Minister and other policy makers in the future.

References

Alderslade, R., Hunter, D. (1992) 'Forward March'. *Health Service Journal.* 19th March 1992: 22–23.

Alimo-Metcalfe, B, Alban-Metcalfe, R. 'Heaven Can Wait' *Health Service Journal* 12th October 2000: 26–29.

Bass, B.B., Avolio, B.J. (1993) 'Transformational Leadership and Organisational Culture'. *PAQ.* Spring 1993: 112–121.

Belasco, J.A. (1990) *Teaching The Elephant to Dance: Empowering Change In Your Organisation.* London: Hutchinson Business Books.

Burnard, P. (1994) 'Searching for Meaning: A Method of Analysing Interview Transcripts with a Personal Computer'. *Nurse Education Today.* Vol 14, 111–117.

Colin-Thome, D. (1996) 'The Total Fundholder'. In G. Meads, (ed.) *Future Options for General Practice.* Oxford: Radcliffe Medical Press.

Coulter, A., Mays, N. (1997) 'Deregulating Primary Care'. *British Medical Journal.* Vol 315, 510–513.

Cresswell, J. (1997) 'US-Style Health Maintenance Organisations Are Likely in Britain'. *British Medical Journal.* Vol 314, 328.

Department of Health (1999a) *Saving lives: our healthier nation* London: Department of Health.

Department of Health (1997) *The new NHS : modern, dependable* London: Department of Health.

Department of Health (1998) *A first class service: quality in the new NHS* London: Department of Health.

Department of Health (1999c) *National service framework for mental health modern standards service models* London: Department of Health.

Department of Health (2000a) *The NHS plan: a plan for investment: a plan for reform* London: Department of Health.

Department of Health (2000b) *National service framework for coronary heart disease: modern standards & service models* London: Department of Health.

Department of Health (2001b) *National service framework for older people: modern standards & service models* London: Department of Health.

Department of Health (2001a). *Shifting the Balance of Power.* London: Department of Health.

Department of Health. (1994) *Towards A Primary Care Led NHS: An Accountability Framework For GP Fundholding EL(94)92.* Leeds: Department of Health.

Department of Health. (1996a) *Primary Care: The Future – Choice and Opportunity.* London: HMSO.

Department of Health. (1996b) *Primary Care: Delivering the Future.* London: HMSO.

Dixon, M., Sweeney, K. (2001) *A Practical Guide to Primary Care Groups and Trusts.* Abingdon: Radcliffe Medical Press.

Garratt, B. (1990) *Learning to Lead: Developing Your Organisation Yourself.* London: Harper Collins.

Glaser, B.G., Strauss, A.L. (1967) *The Discovery of Grounded Theory: Strategies for Qualitative Research.* New York: De Gruyter.

Groves, T. (1997) 'What The Changes Mean'. *British Medical Journal.* Vol 314, 436–438.

Ham, C. (1997) 'Time To Get It Together'. *Health Service Journal.* 20th February 1997: 22.

Hammersley, M., Atkinson, P. (1995) *Ethnography: Principles in Practice.* London: Tavistock.

Higgins, J. (2001) 'Back to the future'. *Health Service Journal* 21st June 2001: 26–27.

Hill, R., Shepherd, G. (1997) 'Joint Resolutions'. *Health Service Journal.* 10th April 1997: 30–31.

Hinterhuber, H.H., Popp, W. (1992) 'Are You a Strategist or Just a Manager?' *Harvard Business Review.* January–February 1992: 105–113.

Kotter, J.P. (1995) 'Leading Change: Why Transformation Efforts Fail'. *Harvard Business Review.* March–April 1995: 59–67.

Management Research Group Gmbh. (1992) *Leadership Effectiveness Analysis: Personal Feedback Profile.* Munchen: Management Research Group GMBH.

McKeon, A.J. (1996) 'Making it Happen'. In G. Meads (ed.) *A Primary Care Led NHS: Putting it into Practice.* Edinburgh: Churchill Livingstone.

Meads, G. (1996) 'The British Dilemma'. In G. Meads, (ed.) *Future Options for General Practice.* Oxford: Radcliffe Medical Press.

Meads, G., Wilkin, D. (1997) 'Preparing For A Primary Care Led NHS: The Future Choice, Risks and Opportunities'. *Primary Care Management.* Vol 7 (1), 3–6.

NHS Executive (1999b) *Clinical governance: quality in the new NHS* London: Department of Health.

NHS Executive. (1994) *Developing NHS Purchasing and GP Fundholding EL(94)79.* Leeds: NHS Executive.

Pearson, P. (1996) 'Towards A Primary Care Led NHS'. *Health Visitor.* Vol 69 (9), 376–378.

Pettigrew, A., Whipp, R. (1991) *Managing Change For Competitive Success.* Oxford: Blackwell.

Pringle, M. (1997) 'An Opportunity To Improve Primary Care'. *British Medical Journal.* Vol 314, 595–597.

Rawnsley, A. (2001) *Servants of the People* London: Penguin Books.

Roberts, W. (1989) *Leadership Secrets of Attila the Hun.* London: Bantam Press.

Robinson, B. (1996) 'Primary Managed Care: the Lyme Alternative'. In G. Meads, (ed). *Future Options For General Practice*. Oxford: Radcliffe Medical Press.

Robinson, R. (1996) 'The Impact of the NHS Reforms 1991–1995: A Review Of The Research Evidence'. *Journal Of Public Health Medicine*. Vol 18 (3), 337–342.

Salter, B., Snee, N. (1997) 'Power Dressing'. *Health Service Journal*. 13th February 1997: 30–31.

Sashkin, M., Rosenbach, W. (1993) 'A New Leadership Paradigm'. In W. Rosenbach, R. Taylor, (eds.) *Contemporary Issues in Leadership*. Boulder: West View Press.

Secretaries of State. (1989) *Working for Patients*. London: HMSO.

Stern, P.N. (1980) 'Grounded Theory: Its Uses and Processes'. *Image*. Vol XII (1), 20–23.

Stewart, D.W., Shamdasani, P.N. (1990) *Focus Groups: Theory and Practice*. California: Sage.

Stewart, R. (1996) *Leading in the NHS: A Practical Guide*. Basingstoke: Macmillan Press.

Wright, P.L. (1996) *Managerial Leadership*. London: Routledge.

■ Dr Ian Cameron MPH, FFPHM, MA is a Consultant in Public Health Medicine at Leeds Health Authority, and Honorary Senior Lecturer at the University of Leeds. His responsibilities include mental health, physical disabilities and learning disabilities. He is also a Board Member of East Leeds Primary Care Group and is leading work on primary care and community services. Recent publications include a major health needs assessment on younger people with dementia, the use of drop in and outreach schemes and an audit on the use of anti-dementia drugs.

CHAPTER FOUR

Towards a model of effective partnership working

Stephanie Stanwick

Foreword

This paper examines some of the critical issues around partnership working in the Health Service.

At the time of writing this paper, I was an Executive Director of a large Health Authority responsible for a resident population of nearly a million people, a budget of £500 million, the services of 8 local Trusts, 210 General Practitioners (GPs), a two tier Local Authority and a new Unitary Local Authority, eight District Councils, four Community Health Councils (CHCs) and nine shadow Primary Care Groups (PCGs).

An integral part of my role was to work in partnership with people from all these organisations to improve local health services, and I became very interested in the critical factors for successful partnership working.

Introduction

The 1998 Government White Paper 'The New NHS – Modern Dependable' placed a statutory duty on NHS organisations to work in partnership with each other and with Local Authorities in developing common goals and health care plans for local communities.

This represented a fundamental shift from the philosophy of competition that had shaped the NHS since 1992. Organisations which had spent six years institutionalising a culture of competitiveness were suddenly expected to develop a culture of partnership with others. GPs – traditionally independent professionals – were expected to learn to work together in groups, not just to improve health care for their own practices, but to improve health care for their locality and their Primary Care Group. Health organisations were expected to work in partnership with Local Authorities on their respective policy agendas to benefit local communities.

To meet the requirements of the White Paper, many collaborative inter-organisational projects have been established. The people who lead such projects need to be able to understand and manage the complexities and dynamics of these partnerships in order to achieve change. I hope this paper can contribute to such an understanding.

Strategic networks, alliances and federations

In the commercial sector, some industries are already exploring strategic partnerships between companies within the same field of production. Jarillo (1993) describes organisations that work so closely together they sometimes provide a single face to the outside world. In the *strategic network,* one company takes the role of central controller and organises the flow of goods amongst other independent organisations.

Strategic networks can provide the long term security of a vertically integrated company whilst retaining the entrepreneurial drive of smaller independent firms, which are able to come up with technological breakthroughs because of their ability to focus on a small range of activities. Jarillo argues that strategic networks provide a way of co-ordinating stable relationships between separate organisations, and that through co-operation the companies can find a way of increasing total and individual returns. *Trust* is at the very core of a strategic network. It is a long-term and purposeful relationship where competitive advantage is obtained by those in the network over those outside it.

Kanter (1989) describes companies as becoming 'PALS' – pooling, allying, and linking across each other. Over time a set of working relationships evolve that gradually institutionalise a strategic alliance.

Several observers have argued that networking and the development of alliances may be basic to organising and managing people in the future and that the concepts of human networks and the process of social networking are the prime components of a properly balanced organisational system in turbulent times (for example, Kaplan and Mazique 1983, Mueller 1991, Kotter 1996). Networks are informal systems, short lived and self camouflaging, they are invisible and unaccountable. Mueller argues that networking provides tremendous power to get ideas accepted or new action underway and can empower an organisation to alter course or to accept change.

There are some lessons here for Health Care Trusts. In most areas of the country there is a need for the NHS to consider the range of specialties each Trust can provide, and in some instances decide how to reconfigure services so that specialties are shared across Trusts and across different sites.

These are not easy relationships to achieve. Trusts are expected to behave altruistically and share specialist services, yet not so long ago each Trust would have competed with the others to provide the same service.

In a similar way, GP practices are expected to come together to work for the good of their collective localities in Primary Care Groups (PCGs). Though the 'competition' between practices is less overt than that between Trusts, GPs do not want to lose people from their lists to other practices – the numbers of people on the list and the income of the practice is inextricably linked.

Handy (1992) argues that *Federal Organisations* are the compromise between open markets and central planning. They are like marriages and are held together by trust and common goals. Within the federal organisational model, power is to be shared and autonomy granted – *subsidiarity* places power at the lowest corporate point, and *interdependence* spreads power around – avoiding the risk of a central bureaucracy. Handy argues that a proper federation needs a common law, language, and a uniform way of doing business, but that twin citizenship ensures a strong federal presence in a strong independent region. Perhaps this is a model for the PCGs/PCTs of the future – GP practices retaining their strong independent identity whilst also being a 'citizen' of the PCG/PCT itself.

The research

I wanted to explore the factors that influence successful working across organisational boundaries and partnership working

I intended to interview ten leaders of inter-organisational projects, all of whom were considered to be successful. In the event, I was able to interview eight of them in the time available.

They came from a variety of backgrounds including:

• the Leader of a GP Total Purchasing Pilot Project

- a Manager who was leading a GP Commissioning Project involving local Mental Health Services
- a Director of a Community and Mental Health Trust responsible for partnership projects
- a GP leader of a GP Commissioning Pilot Project
- a Senior Police Officer responsible for inter-agency working at Police authority level
- A Senior Manager in Social Services responsible for a joint commissioning project in Learning Disability Services
- a Director of a Health Authority responsible for partnership working
- a GP working across a number of practices to develop local services.

Most of the interviewees spoke very freely and openly about the projects with which they were involved.

This is a small sample, but as Henry Mintzberg (1979) argues, relatively simple research methodologies have produced more useful results than those which have been significant only in the statistical sense.

The interviews generated a great deal of detailed information. I used processes of grounded theory and analytic induction to analyse and categorise this information, and to build links between the categories (Gill and Johnson 1997, Strauss and Corbin 1990).

Figure 1 shows the categories that emerged from these interviews and how they are linked, using some of the actual words from one interview in each of the linked categories.

The categories and sub-categories were linked by a pattern of relationships:

- *causal conditions* are the events or incidents that triggered the partnership project. In the projects I explored, the main triggers were government policies, local controversies or service problems
- *context* influences the shape of projects. The most significant contextual factors were the formal and informal characteristics of the partner organisations
- *intervening conditions* that contributed to the success of the projects included the cultures that were developed within the project groups, and the personal attributes of the project leaders (and key members of the groups)

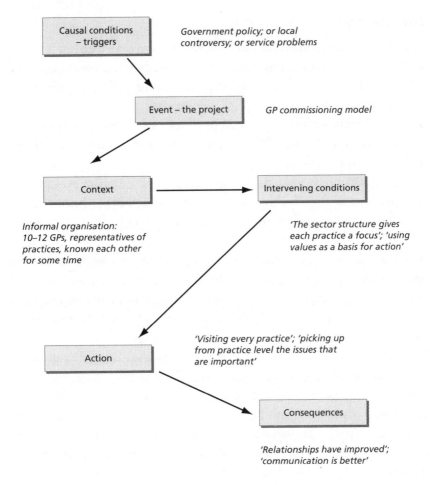

Figure 1: A model for partnership working

- *action/interaction strategies* were particular behaviours that contributed to success
- *consequences* concerned both the outcomes for the particular aims of the project, and the outcomes for continued partnership working.

From these patterns it is possible to suggest some critical factors that will support successful partnership working across organisational boundaries, and even to suggest factors that will be most important in particular types of partnership.

The findings

One of the natural difficulties in achieving effective partnership working between Health Sector organisations has already been mentioned: the recent (and to some extent still present) state of competition between individual organisations.

Other difficulties are represented by differences between organisations – in particular, different priorities, differences in structures and systems, and differences in values.

Different priorities may arise simply from the different positions of organisations in the Health Care system. For example, a priority for a Health Authority could be equity of access to good quality mental health services for people with problems – but this might not be so important to a GP practice that perceives its own practice population to be well served (even if a neighbouring practice is not). The Health Authority and the GP practice might also place different relative priorities on the needs of different groups – such as the mentally ill, say, as compared to the needs of older people.

There are obvious differences in structures and systems between health care organisations. For example, an NHS Trust may employ 2000 staff, whereas a GP practice may only employ a handful. The Trust has a Chief Executive and a board with heads of departments (whatever they might be titled), whereas the practice is a professional legal partnership. There are some similarities but many differences between the large, formal bureaucratic organisations of Trusts and local authorities, on the one hand, and the smaller, more informal GP practices on the other. These are significant, not superficial differences.

Different organisational structures are likely to make it difficult to identify where the responsibility sits for making decisions. For example, at an operational level, a health care worker and a social worker may both be empowered to take operational decisions about the care of a patient, but they will probably have very different levels of influence when it comes to strategic decision making.

Understanding how these differences might impact on partnership working is important for successful collaborative working.

In addition to structures and systems, values and cultures are also important issues.

For example, if one organisation is prepared to take risks in working jointly with another, and wants to be innovative and encourage initiative, whilst the other organisation wants to maintain control and take no risks, this of itself will create issues for a partnership venture.

Globerman and Mintzberg (1994) argue that there are in reality four components of the health care system (cure, care, control and community) disconnected by their unreconciled values, inconsistent structures, and intransigent attitudes. All four have different organising principles including administrative hierarchies, professional chimneys, formal boards and co-ordination of care. All of these points reinforce difficulties of working across different health care settings in order to provide integrated care.

From the interviews I found that the different organisational types – which I classed simply as ranging from formal (hierarchical, bureaucratic) to informal (smaller, less proceduralised) – had a significant bearing on the actions and processes that people adopted within the projects in order to get things done. The greatest dissonance was evident in those projects which involved both highly formal and highly informal types of organisation, simply because of the different processes and actions each organisation would naturally choose to adopt.

For example, an informal 'club' organisation of GPs *believe* that working together will produce sustainable improvement. They adopt a structure which will enable their goals, values and beliefs to be developed, and they value personal attributes such as 'acting as a bridge'. This affects the way they choose to get things done – they visit every practice, they get groups to look at particular issues, they use a facilitating process.

Figure 2 shows the action/interaction strategies that this informal organisation uses to progress within in its own organisational framework – and also strategies that it would use working across organisational boundaries into a more formal organisation.

This contrasts with a formal, hierarchical organisation whose members identify a problem they can't solve on their own – they need others to help. This organisation can usually get things done by 'telling' staff to do them. The process they would choose to adopt is that of senior people getting together, deciding what needs to be done, and then making things happen back in their own respective organisations (and agreeing how to overcome the 'bottleneck' of middle management). This is shown in

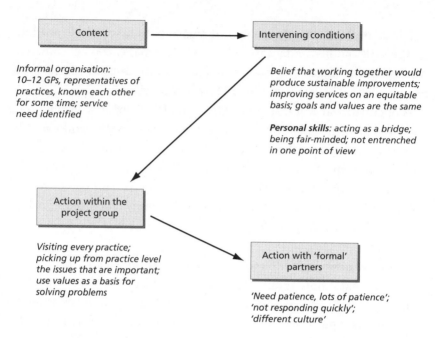

Figure 2: The relationship between organisational characteristics, personal attributes and effective action: informal organisations working with formal partners

Figure 3 – both how the organisation would work within in its own boundaries, and the action strategies that it would like to use when working across its boundaries, into another formal organisation.

The dissonance between the different types of organisation is likely to give rise to some of the negative aspects of process strategies: i.e. feelings of frustration, getting bogged down, of there being a cultural divide. There is what could be described as a '*cultural intolerance*' or a '*cultural prejudice*' between organisations at different points on the continuum between formal and informal. This means that managers leading such projects need to become familiar with the 'cultural diversity' that they have to deal with, and understand the relationships between an organisation's culture and the processes that it would choose to adopt if left to its own devices.

Problems were not restricted to projects between different types of organisation, however. I found that some dissonance in project processes

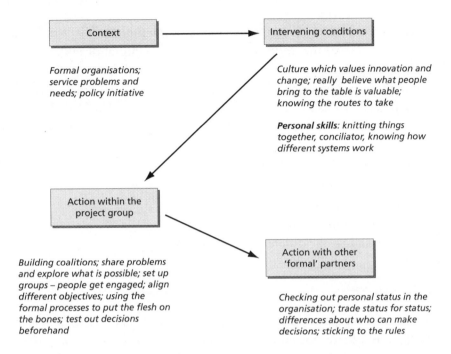

Figure 3: The relationship between organisational characteristics, personal attributes and effective action: informal organisations working with formal partners

could also occur where two different *highly formal* organisations were involved in working together.

Successful leaders of partnership projects have the personal skills and knowledge to manage such complexities, choosing a course of action that can be adapted, explaining to each 'side' why things happen or why the organisation behaves in the way it does.

All the project leaders I interviewed emphasised that the amount of time required to achieve change is greatly underestimated. They described processes that relied as much on the informal approaches of networking, alliances and relationships, as they did on formal approaches to project management.

The leadership style of the person heading the project can have a fundamental effect on the culture of the project group, and the success of the project. The leader's ideas about the appropriate beliefs and values for the project team will be tested early on in the process and, if successful, will start to form part of the founding culture of the project. This reinforces the importance of the leader understanding the cultural diversity of the participating organisations, and it might suggest that some of the dissonance in project processes is generated early on in the life of the project.

Significant *personal attributes* of project leaders identified through the interviews were:

- Being supportive/helpful/listening
- Respecting differences
- Openness/integrity
- Good communication
- Understanding the different ways of doing things

Summary

The model for partnership working in the NHS developed from this study demonstrates the complex dynamics that projects encounter when working with a range of different partners. The difficulties should not be underestimated. Projects that operate across organisational boundaries must take into account the type of organisations they are working with; their structure, forms, and accountabilities; their culture and processes. This requires, from all those who participate, an investment in people and time, and a flexibility in approach.

This study indicates some the skills and processes that appear to be effective in partnership working, and suggests some of the key contingent factors that are involved.

The final version of the model is seen in Figure 4.

The model developed in this study provides a practical conceptual framework for some of the organisational issues involved in partnership working.

There are practical lessons for the leadership and management of these projects which include:

- the value of understanding the values and principles of the participants;
- being able to devise a marriage of approaches for the required project processes;

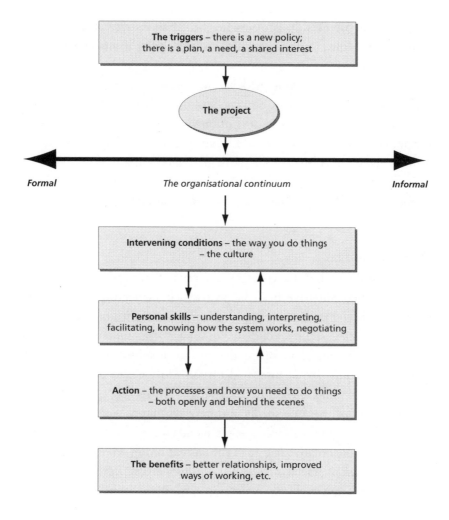

Figure 4: A model of partnership working

- being able to articulate realistic expectations for all who contribute both at an organisational or individual level;
- being prepared to work behind the scene using informal systems and contacts to influence progress;
- being prepared to act as an interpreter of one organisation's behaviour to another;
- being 'culturally tolerant' of all organisations involved.

Leaders of partnership projects need to demonstrate creative change management skills, leadership skills, and the ability to manage complexity and diversity.

Over time, there is some evidence that projects produce an environment where the differences become less of an issue, where the understanding between partners is institutionalised as a part of the culture of the project. Over time, as this understanding grows, it begins to impact a little on the main culture of the participating organisations. As more successful partnership projects take place, perhaps over time the competitive culture in the NHS will change to a more collaborative one.

Postscript

I am currently a Chief Executive of a Primary Care Trust, established in October 2000, and have been in post a year. Reflecting on this paper from my current post reinforces the current relevance of these themes. Many of my chief executive colleagues in similar organisations describe them as 'federal' reflecting some of the descriptors of subsidiarity and interdependence (Handy 1992) discussed earlier. Most health economies have cancer networks and clinical networks high on their list of priorities; the characteristics of these networks also have resonance with the literature. The NHS Plan and the Government's agenda for modernising health care reinforce the collaborative nature of the current health service environment

The personal characteristics and skills of leaders reflected in this paper are the ones I am seeking to develop within my own organisation. I expect managers to be able to demonstrate skills which are supportive/helpful/listening, and that respect the differences of the different organisations. I want managers who can understand, and be flexible and comfortable about the very different ways of doing things that apply in different organisations. They need to manage projects where they openly value the different values and principles of the different participants, they need to devise a marriage of the various approaches for managing processes, to articulate realistic expectations for all who contribute both at an organisational and an individual level, to use informal systems and contacts to influence progress and to act as an interpreter of one organisation's behaviour to another, being 'culturally tolerant' of all organisations involved.

References

Gill, J., Johnson, P. (1997) *Research Methods for Managers,* Paul Chapman Publishing.

Globerman, S., Mintzberg, H. (1994) *Managing the Care of Health and the Cure of Disease,* Paper, 1994, based on research and seminars with the support of the King Edward's Hospital Fund, September 1994.

Handy, C. (1992) *Balancing Corporate Power, A New Federalist Paper* Harvard Business Review, November–December 1992.

Kanter, R.M. (1989) *When Giants Learn to Dance, Managing the Challenges of Strategy Management and Careers in the 1990s* Unwin Paperbacks.

Kaplan, R.E., Mazique, M. (1983) *Trade Routes: The Managers Network of Relationships,* Report No 22, Centre for Creative Leadership, Yale University 1983.

Kotter, J. (1996) *Leading Change,* Harvard Business School Press.

Mintzberg, H. (1979) *An Emerging Strategy of 'Direct' Research,* Administrative Science Quarterly, Vol 24, December pp 582–9.

Mueller, R.K. (1991) 'Corporate Networking, How to Tap Unconventional Wisdom', in Henry, J. (Ed) (1991) *Creative Management,* London Sage Publications.

Strauss, A., Corbin, J. (1990) *Basics of Qualitative Research, Grounded Theory Procedures and Techniques* Sage Publications.

■ Stephanie Stanwick is the Chief Executive Officer of Dartford, Gravesham and Swanley Primary Care Trust. After a long nursing career in Acute Hospitals, she went into Nursing Research and Practice Development before moving into General Management and in 1995 she became Director of Commissioning at West Kent. She has been in her present post since August 2000. She says in reality she has been lucky enough to have two NHS careers (in Nursing and General Management) which gives her a very special understanding of the NHS. Her family life keeps her sane (most of the time).

CHAPTER FIVE

The competencies required for effective partnership working between health and local authority managers

John Kitson

A recurring theme of the Labour Government's plans for modernising the NHS has been the requirement for collaborative or partnership working between the various organisations involved in the planning and delivery of health services. This paper explores the management competencies which will be required to advance partnerships at the specific interface of health and local authorities.

Just as barriers exist between professions, organisational barriers exist both between, and within, health and social care organisations. Stewart (1996) perceptively identifies those difficulties which are particular barriers when people have to work together in the health and social care arena. These include:

> 'The natural tendency for people to identify with their own group and be suspicious of outsiders; mutual ignorance of each other's work; external pressures upon one or both organisations; conflicting interests of diverse groups; professionals' beliefs that they know best and that public views are uninformed and mistaken; and difficulties with particular organisations.'
>
> Stewart, 1996, p88–99

The consultation paper, *Partnership in Action* (1998) offered proposals for how health and social services can work together, including possibilities for pooled budgets and for easier cross-over in providing services across health and social care. These proposals together with the Health Action Zone programme, indicated a policy of encouraging services which focus on care pathways for individuals rather than on organisational structures. This underlined the need for health service organisations to operate in ways that go beyond narrow views of the functions of one organisation.

There are many obstacles to achieving this. Some of these are institutional obstacles, such as the different political accountabilities and legal responsibilities of health and local authorities.

More significantly still, partnerships are about trust and confidence in one another; these can only be developed between the individuals concerned. Simons (1998) has argued that to adapt, managers will need to '... develop 'diplomacy and reconciliation' skills to get people from different organisations and backgrounds working together'. They would also need to use '... networking, negotiation and facilitation to achieve their goals'. Simons admitted that nobody '... knows what managers will come into work and actually do in five years time'.

Within this context of managerial adaptation and skill development, a suitable starting point is to identify the competencies required for effective partnership working. And although there are various models of management competency, there appear to be few which specifically address partnership working.

What are competencies?

'Competencies are behavioural repertoires that some people can carry out better than other people.'

Woodruffe, 1993, p67

'[They are] characteristics that are causally related to effective and/or superior performance in a job. This means that there is evidence that indicates that possession of the characteristic precedes and leads to effective and/or superior performance in that job.'

Boyatzis, 1982, p23

Boyatzis' definition highlights the aspect of causality – ie evidence that the underlying characteristic *leads* to effective and/or superior performance.

Spencer & Spencer (1993) are more direct in saying that 'Causally-related means that a competency *causes* or *predicts* behaviour and performance'.

The research

I carried out detailed interviews, using a Behavioural Event approach, with six people who were:

• working in the Health Service/Local Authority interface
• involved in partnership working
• effective at partnership working as judged by opposite numbers and/or peers.

The selection was assisted by colleagues currently working in the area of partnership between health and local authorities.

Spencer and Spencer draw attention to the advantage of Behavioural Event Interviews (BEI) over direct observation with the following encouraging comment,

> Done correctly, the BEI method gathers critical incident information equivalent to direct observation data, but much more efficiently. A 60 to 90 minute interview can produce almost as much usable data as a week of intensive observation or a year of regular work activity
>
> Spencer & Spencer, 1993, p104

I asked each interviewee to recall a specific past occurrence in the area of partnership working between health and local authorities in which they felt particularly successful or positive about the outcome. Thereafter they were asked to relate their own thoughts, words and deeds at each point in the event. The aim was to uncover raw data on the interviewee's behaviour, avoiding as far as possible, any generalisations which led to the successful or positive outcome.

One criticism of the Behavioural Event Interview technique relates to the accuracy of recall of the interviewees, and the natural tendency of individuals to use hindsight in rationalising the past. I took steps to minimise this danger by asking interviewees to recall relatively recent critical incidents, and to limit their responses to describing what they were *actually* doing, saying, thinking at the time of the incident.

To assist in describing the competency behaviours, I used the dictionary of competencies from Spencer & Spencer (1993), and also the ideas of Kotter (1995) on transformational change and Moss Kanter (1989) on partnerships.

I originally identified a total of 63 behaviours from the interviews.

I returned my first draft of the competency behaviours that emerged from the interviews to the interviewees themselves, in questionnaire form, and asked them to rate the relevance of each competency behaviours on a 1 (low relevance) to 5 (high relevance). Only those competencies which scored on average 3.6 or more were included in the final model – there were 21 behaviours in all. Four of the behaviours were drawn from the Spencer & Spencer (1993) Competency Model, the rest were newly-defined for this study.

I used a relatively high discriminating threshold score to validate the developed competency behaviours, and some of the behaviours I rejected at this stage may have a degree of relevance to effective partnership working, but they were not identified as significant by the majority of interviewees/respondents in this study. Further testing of the rejected behaviours with a wider group of respondents may lead to additions to the model in the future.

I clustered the competency behaviours under four headlines, three of which are drawn from Spencer and Spencer:

- Achievement and action
- Impact and influence
- Partnership building
- Personal effectiveness

Partnership competencies

Achievement and action

The central emphasis in the achievement and action competency is on *acting for change*. Behind each of the five behaviours the motivating force is a drive to bring about change on a partnership wide basis. Another important facet of the achievement and action competency is the concern for the *process* of the implementation of change.

- Consciously maintains a clear focus on the desired partnership objectives
- Recognises and seizes opportunities*
- Is persistent, refuses to give up when faced with obstacles and rejection*
- Plans ahead to enable partners to fully participate in joint discussions and decision making
- Negotiates and agrees frameworks or processes to assure implementation of changes

---

*These behaviours are taken from the Spencer and Spencer (1993) model

Impact and influence

This competency concerns the development of personal networks and from this, the ability to appreciate the complete 'picture' of the partnership work under discussion. To gain awareness of partner organisations, effective managers take the initiative in investing time in getting to know how partners work, and in building personal relationships.

The second feature of this competency is the communication of 'messages which may not be apparent to others', and the use of personal authority and group process skills to lead or direct a group – in other words, the use of influence.

- Actively works at communicating messages which may not be apparent to others
- Carries sufficient authority within own organisation to accurately represent its views and properly negotiate with partners on its behalf
- Uses 'group process skills' to lead or direct a group*
- Understands the other partners' worlds and also how oneself is perceived, so that credible proposals for change can be made
- Makes a conscious effort to discover and understand the way partner organisations work so as to recognise organisational constraints – what is and is not possible at certain times or in certain positions

---

*These behaviours are taken from the Spencer and Spencer (1993) model

Partnership building

This competency has links with the achievement and action behaviours in relation to desired outcomes. It is probably more to do with *how* such outcomes are determined eg through building rapport and relationships, the *quality* of the desired outcomes, and the need to keep them constantly in view as a means of forming and building a partnership.

The ability to use facilitative interventions appears to be fundamental to the competency behaviours identified in partnership building.

- Works to ensure partners are always seeking the same desired outcomes and these are both specific and explicit
- Enables people to be free to share their personal or organisational views so that the operating environment can be accurately established
- Consciously works at building rapport*
- Checks that all partners believe desired outcomes are sufficiently worthwhile to drive concern and action to achieve them

---

*These behaviours are taken from the Spencer and Spencer (1993) model

Personal effectiveness

On the whole, these behaviours characterise a personal commitment to partnership working that probably springs from a belief that this way of working is necessary to achieve effective change and improvements for patients and clients. 'Whole Systems' considerations underlie this competency, as do the concepts of continuous improvement and personal learning.

- Chooses to meet partnership working needs rather than to pursue narrow professional interests
- Doesn't dwell on past failures of partnership working but faces up to previous poor performance in order to improve
- Actively listens to those stakeholders who are having difficulty in reaching partnership agreements and is willing to encourage and empower them
- Acts resolutely on principles once these have been agreed with partners
- Is explicit on options which may be desirable and involve significant change
- When necessary, takes the lead to ensure progress if the partnership's objectives and agenda is maintained
- Changes own behaviour or approach to suit the situation

In a sense, whole systems thinking is integral to effective partnership working. Taking a whole systems view necessarily requires exploration of new territories, looking into other organisational worlds and devising ways of including partners in structures, systems and processes that will deliver the desired strategic outcomes.

Whole systems thinking and planning has only recently been overtly articulated in the NHS and Social Services. It has begun to be expressed in relation to emergency care services and waiting list initiatives. It was well expressed in the NHS Executive Emergency Services Action Report (ESAT), (1998) though even here it was acknowledged that '... it tends to have different meanings in different settings'.

For example in some hospitals 'whole system' means considering elective and non-elective surgery as a whole system, with waiting lists as something unrelated to either – but a genuine whole system perspective must include at least all three. Beyond the hospital, the linkages to primary care/community services and social services are equally critical. The ability to think in these terms does not come easily to a health and social service system which has been built on specialisation and different funding regimes. In the main, this is true at an organisational and personal level.

The role of *fostering and facilitating co-operation* is interesting, and is at one with the Personal Effectiveness behaviours identified for effective partnership working. In reality however, it poses problems for many managers who are mostly assessed on maintaining the status quo by ensuring 'their part of the system' meets budget and is not exposed to risk. Only those managers who are open to change and see eventual benefits for patients and clients will be motivated to behave in the way this competency requires.

Application

This is a limited initial study, but I believe that the four partnership competencies identified in this study can be used to support and develop senior managers who work across the interface of health service and local government organisations.

Since the initial research, feedback from several discussion sessions with NHS Senior Managers on the partnership competencies has been very positive. The competencies have proved to be of particular interest to Health Authority Performance Managers and Directors who need to work in partnership with Primary Care Trusts (PCTs).

It would be useful to validate these competency behaviours further, and to check on the relevance of some of the behaviours omitted from this final model, with a larger group – and this may be a project for the future.

The model should also be assessed, on a regular basis, for three key characteristics which are identified by Boak (1998) as making the difference between more-effective and less-effective competency models. These are:

- accuracy, which is to do with comprehensiveness and adequacy of the competency descriptions. This may change over time as circumstances change;
- acceptability, based on proximity to the experience of users and integration with other task priorities, initiatives and skills that apply to the user; and,
- accessibility, which concerns ease of understanding and application.

In using the competencies for management development, the first stage should be discussions with managers, probably in small groups. The very act of discussing partnership competencies by sharing experience and the thinking behind it, has potential to begin the process of development.

This approach should be supplemented through a simple assessment matrix that could include self, peer and external contact assessment measured against the partnership competencies.

To date, many of the partnership competencies that emerged from this study are being confirmed as relevant to influence PCTs and other partner organisations, in order to agree and to achieve targets that benefit both patients and the public.

References

Boak, G. (1998) *Benchmarks for competency models.* London: Competency Volume 5, Number 2, Winter 1997/98, IRS Eclipse Group.

Boyatzis, R.E., (1982) *The Competent Manager – A Model for Effective Performance.* New York, USA: John Wiley & Sons.

Kanter, R.M. (1989) *When Giants Learn To Dance.* London: International Thomson Business Press.

Kanter, R.M. (1994) *Learning to Collaborate.* Harvard Business Review, August 1994.

Klemp, G.O., Jr (Ed.) (1980) *The assessment of occupational competence.* Washington USA: Report to the National Institute of Education, cited in Boyatzis, R.E., (1982) The Competent Manager: A Model for Effective Performance. New York: Wiley

Kotter, J.P. (1995) *Why Transformation Efforts Fail.* Harvard Business Review, March–April 1995.

NHS Executive (1998) *Emergency Services Action Team 1998 Report.* Department of Health: London.

Owens, D. (1998) *Joint Working – Duel Carriageway.* Ruislip, Middlesex: Health Service Journal, Volume 107, 22 October 1998.

Simons, B. (1998) *Proceedings of the 1998 Annual Conference of the Association of Chartered Certified Accountants Health Service Society.* Ruislip, Middlesex: Heath Service Journal, Volume 107, 22 October 1998.

Spencer, L.M. Jnr & Spencer, S.M. (1993) *Competence at Work: Models for Superior Performance.* Toronto, Canada: John Wiley & Sons Inc.

Stewart, R. (1996) *Leading in the NHS – A Practical Guide.* London: Macmillan Press Ltd.

Woodruffe, C. (1993) *Assessment Centres: Identifying and Developing Competence.* London: Institute of Personnel Management.

CHAPTER SIX

Key characteristics of successful partnership working

Thelma Holland

Introduction

In 1997, some six months after coming into office, the Labour Government published the White Paper 'The New NHS, Modern, Dependable'. The vision for the NHS laid out in this document saw a move away from the market orientation of the previous Conservative Government towards the establishment of collaborative partnerships to achieve seamless care, with clearly identified performance requirements.

The principle of separating the purchaser/commissioner and provider functions was to remain and, as pointed out by Goddard and Mannion (1998), this requires the development of high trust relationships. In those cities in the UK which have more than one large hospital, decades of rivalry had been honed to perfection during the years of the internal market! Establishing collaborative partnerships between these organisations would be challenging.

In the late summer of 1999, cognisant of the major influences impacting on large teaching hospitals, two hospitals in a large provincial English city – the City Hospital and the University Hospital – undertook an appraisal of the advantages and disadvantages of merger, or of a purposeful structured partnership. After a series of consultative meetings with staff, the decision was to develop a partnership approach.

The decision was based on a shared conviction that there were benefits for patients of closer working between the two hospitals – as well as benefits for staff, and other partner organisations – which could be achieved without the upheaval and inertia of a merger process. The two organisations were very different in style, culture and approach.

Once the decision was taken, the two hospitals committed considerable executive, senior management and clinician time to getting to know and understand each other better, and to building shared purpose, a shared vision of what hospital services will look like in the city in the future and a shared strategy to achieve that vision. A partnership framework was developed to address issues of accountability and governance.

As Chief Executive of one of the hospitals, I was closely involved in this activity. This paper describes an assessment of the partnership at an early stage in the process, in the first six months of the work being done to bring the two organisations closer together.

Partnerships and mergers

The private sector has, for some time, seen a move towards the establishment of strategic alliances, formed for a variety of reasons, many rooted in the drive for greater market share and profitability. The rationale for strategic alliances, however, has congruence within the Health Service –faith that organisations will be stronger together than separately; that each partner will contribute skills and abilities the other lacks; a belief that costs can be reduced through increasing economy of scale and that technology can be shared.

The literature suggests that successful strategic alliances are difficult to achieve and that failures abound (eg Dyer et al 2001). Merger or acquisition appear no easier to achieve successfully, and research points to increasing costs, high staff turnover, inertia, and reduction in performance in many merged companies. There have been problems associated with NHS mergers – one survey notes a failure to deliver benefits in 70% of cases, organisational stress, reduction in performance, increased absenteeism, increase in staff disputes, reduction in quality standards and defections (THS 1998). Another study suggests that merger may increase cost and inhibit reconfiguration of services (Newchurch 1998). The Newchurch report recommends instead co-operative behaviour reflecting the community of interest, and stresses the potential for co-operation between organisations with common goals, whilst remaining autonomous.

Developing strategic alliances and partnerships take time. The partners need to build trust between the organisations, often in the face of very different corporate cultures and management styles. There needs to be compatibility of strategic aim and clearly defined objectives for the alliance.

It seems clear that successful partnerships have certain characteristics, including complementarity, shared vision, common values, clearly defined strategy with goals and milestones, commitment and enthusiasm at the highest levels, and trust. Successful partnerships do not start with all that – it is developed over time and with considerable effort.

I used the framework of the Partnership Assessment Tool (PAT) to evaluate attitudes towards the partnership (Hardy et al 2000). The PAT was produced by the Nuffield Institute for Health, in association with the NHS Executive Trent. It is in harmony with the wider body of research and literature on partnerships, and it identifies six characteristics or principles of successful partnerships:

1 The need for partnership is recognised and accepted
2 There is clarity and realism of purpose with shared vision, values, principles, aims and objectives
3 There is senior commitment to the partnership and consistency of commitment within
4 Trust is developed and maintained through equal status and fairness in the distribution of partnership benefits
5 The partnership arrangements are robust and clear, particularly in relation to responsibilities and accountabilities
6 Monitoring and learning takes place against agreed success criteria

Each of the six principles is defined in more detail in terms of indicative behaviours. The PAT can be used as a questionnaire to audit the health, or otherwise, of a partnership.

Evaluating the partnership

I used focus groups, interviews and a small survey to evaluate attitudes towards the partnership. The various methods of eliciting information complemented each other, each providing a distinctive perspective. The information that was collected was, naturally, put to good use in guiding actions to strengthen the partnership.

Focus groups were held to provide in-depth discussion and information on the key aspects of partnership working, the progress to date and issues still to be addressed. The groups were facilitated to ensure progress and to ensure that any unacceptable behaviours could be dealt with constructively. Their particular value came from the interaction within the groups producing a collective, rather than individual point of view.

One group meeting was with the Executive Directors of both hospitals. The facilitator, who had planned the event with me, was external to the two Trusts. The event was for a whole day and was held at the end of November 1999 – early in the development of the partnership. The main outcomes, taking the partnership forward, were the development of a statement of the partnership context, a statement of the partnership principles and values, the initiation of work to develop an integrated vision/strategy for hospital services, a partnership programme, identifying all the various work streams and the timescales, and an enhanced understanding between the executive teams of the two organisations.

A large workshop for key internal stakeholders (Executives, all Clinical Directors and Heads of Departments) was held in March 2000, with 95 attendees. During the afternoon eight focus groups took place simultaneously, with 10/12 participants in each. This was the last event during the research period being held in March 2000.

Four interviews took place between November 1999, and February 2000, with an incoming Chief Executive, a Chief Executive from within the health community, and senior figures from Primary Care and Regional Office.

I also issued a questionnaire to 50 people closely involved in developing the partnership. I had originally intended to develop an independent questionnaire, seeking local views on the key characteristics of a good partnership, but at the time, local health partnerships in the region were all being circulated with the PAT asked to complete it and I thought the response would have been 'tainted' by the PAT. Pragmatically, therefore, I used the PAT to assess the status and health of the partnership. The respondents targeted for the survey were chosen because of their involvement in, or close association with, the partnership project. They included Executive and Non-executive Directors of both Trusts, chief executives and chairs of local PCGs, health authority staff, staff from other Trusts and staff from the wider health community including Regional Office and Social Services. A letter was sent with the PAT, indicating that the information was being sought primarily to help further develop the collaborative partnership between the hospitals.

Findings

The main messages about the process from the March focus groups, as judged by frequency and strength of articulation, related to:

a Communication – more needed and in different formats to reach different audiences.
b Clarity about benefits for patients, as distinct from benefits for organisations, staff, or managers.
c Development of shared priorities and objectives.
d Being realistic about what we could achieve within what timescale – unless we had the resources to free up more managerial and clinical time to input, and
e Involving Primary Care more and sooner.

The interactive, iterative process of making decisions about the partnership was endorsed, but questions were raised about the earlier involvement of external stakeholders. Some questioned whether the development of a hospital services strategy, and the partnership framework itself, should not be led by the Health Authority. Others wanted more Primary Care involvement at an early stage. There was concern about a strategy being developed which did not reflect the needs of the local environment and local commissioners.

There was, in fact, no evidence that Primary Care felt excluded from the process at this stage. The issue was whether to engage with all partners from the outset, thus demonstrating openness and commitment to wider partnerships, whilst acknowledging that this would reveal differences and unresolved questions.

Across all aspects of the work, there was recognition of the need to involve users/patients, carers and the wider community in the development of strategy and partnership.

One aspect frequently mentioned was that of 'managing expectations'. A great many people feared that there would be unrealistic expectations regarding achievement and timescales within the two organisations, and externally. Many indicated that the health care system was increasingly intolerant of failure, and they were apprehensive about the ability to deliver against such high expectations.

All the interviewees made reference to the significance of the development of a hospital strategy for the city. A major debating point emerged as to who should lead this work – the Trusts, the Health Authority, the health community or Primary Care? There was some scepticism as to whether acute teaching hospitals could read the environment correctly and respond appropriately, and also line up the powerful forces within the hospitals in the preferred direction of travel.

The survey

Thirty-seven responses were received to the survey, a response rate of 74%. Score sheets were completed showing the aggregated profile score (ie the total of all six principles) and the mean score for each of the six principles, as in Table 1.

The possible range for the overall aggregate profile score is 36–144, where:

- 36 indicates that the partnership is working badly;
- 42–72 indicates that the partnership is working well in some respects, but these are outweighed by areas of concern;
- 72–108 indicates that the partnership is working well overall but some aspects may need further exploration;
- 114–144 indicates that the partnership is working well enough in all or most respects.

A score is also shown for each of the six principles. The possible range here is 6–24. The higher the score, the more positive the response to all the requirements/characteristics of that principle.

Table 1 identifies the overall mean score and the scores for each principle, analysed by the different categories of respondent.

Most of the principle scores are in the range 13–18, which indicated that there was some degree of acceptance of the principles and progress was being made.

Table 1: Partnership profile scores by principle and by respondent

| Category of respondent | Aggregate profile score | Principle (mean scores) | | | | | |
		1 Need for partnership	2 Realism of purpose	3 Commitment	4 Trust	5 Working arrangement	6 Monitoring
Trust 1	103.6	19.2	13.3	18.7	18.7	16.5	17.3
Trust 2	105.0	19.1	14.0	19.2	19.2	16.7	17.2
Trust Executives	98.5	18.5	12.9	17.6	17.6	15.5	14.5
Trust Non-Executives	112.0	19.9	14.4	20.7	20.6	17.8	18.4
Primary Care	100.0	17.0	13.7	19.7	18.4	15.2	15.8
Health Community	85.4	13.9	12.7	16.0	14.6	14.7	13.6
Overall	**99.0**	**17.5**	**13.5**	**18.5**	**18.0**	**15.7**	**16.0**

A few scores are in the highest range (19–24) indicating significant progress.

Three principles score persistently higher than the others

- the understanding and the need for partnership
- the level of commitment and ownership, and
- the level of trust

The lowest scores are in the category of clarity and realism of purpose (principle 2) which addresses issues of shared vision, shared values, joint aims and objectives.

The highest scores across the six principles are given by the Non-Executive Directors of both Trusts, who not only score higher than their Executive Director colleagues, but on the three highest scoring principles (see above), give scores in the highest category.

The lowest scores are given by the health community, excluding Primary Care.

The use of the Assessment Tool gave useful baseline information about the perceived success of the partnership to date. The partnership approach had only been agreed in September 1999, so when this survey was undertaken there was only six months of experience of the new arrangements. Partnerships take time to build and mature. In that light I viewed the response positively. Target areas for future attention were identified, both in terms of the work between the two hospitals and also in relation to the involvement of the wider health and social care community.

Principles of partnership

In this section I have summarised what I found in relation to each of the six principles of the Partnership Assessment Tool, with a seventh heading concerning organisational culture.

Principle 1: Recognition and acceptance of the need for partnership

The two hospitals have a history of rivalry and competition – but also a good track record of certain services working across the two sites in the interests of benefits for patients (eg emergency care arrangements, health care of the elderly).

The outcomes from the focus group discussions and the interviews suggest that there was widespread understanding of the factors which make for successful partnerships. References made to staff changes at a senior level, to timescale, expectations and differences in style and culture of the two hospitals clearly indicate an awareness some of the barriers.

According to Cravens et al (1993) high environmental turbulence, coupled with skill and resource gaps, should tend organisations towards strategic alliances rather than merger. However, in an NHS beset by mergers on all fronts, there are likely to be those who persist in calls for merger. It seemed that the partnership would need to demonstrate most, if not all, the characteristics of success and deliver some 'quick wins' to quieten the merger lobby – even if there is no evidence to point for the success of mergers!

In light of the discussion about the strategic options and the work done to identify characteristics of success, the score for overall partnership working and for this particular principle (ie that the need for partnership is recognised and accepted) reflected positively on the work to date.

Principle 2: Clarity and realism of purpose

This principle scored least well across all respondents. The elements included within the principle are:

- Shared vision, values and principles
- Joint aims and objectives, related to outcomes (benefits) for users
- Aims and objectives are realistic
- Acknowledgement of separate organisational aims and objectives and their relationship to joint aims and objectives is understood
- Understanding of extent to which separate aims and objectives enhance or compromise joint aims and objectives
- Focus on likely success

Although scoring against these elements was the lowest achieved in the audit, a mean score of 13.5 puts the assessment within the overall category of 'there is some degree of purpose and reality to the partnership'.

At the time of the survey, the partnership had established an iterative process of staff and stakeholder involvement to develop these elements. This was supported by joint working on a number of infrastructure issues.

This developmental work led to debate between the senior executives as to the most appropriate process. The options were described as 'top down' or 'bottom up' with each hospital having a preference for the approach which most fitted their corporate culture and organisational arrangements. The compromise was the development of initial thoughts at executive level which were then taken through an iterative process internally and externally, to develop and refine.

Discussion was needed at Board level regarding what is, and is not, partnership business and the inter-dependence between the two.

Principle 3: Commitment and ownership

This area scored well on the partnership audit, achieving scores in the highest category from Trust 2, from Trust Non-Executives, and from Primary Care. For all other respondents the scores were well within the category of 'there is some degree of commitment to, and ownership of, the partnership'.

There was also positive feedback regarding commitment from the focus groups and from the individual interviews. Some queries were raised which relate to elements contained in this principle:

- Stability of the senior teams and whether turnover presented threats to successful partnership working; and
- The insufficiency of networking skills across the two hospitals (and across the health community) and hence vulnerability to loss of these skills.

To stabilise the position of the senior team, incoming executives had been recruited on the basis of a commitment to a partnership approach. The lack of skills in networking was of concern and needed to be addressed during future recruitment, particularly the recruitment of a Partnership Programme Manager – an organisational development appointment, with responsibility for the development process and for engagement of key stakeholders.

Principle 4: Development and maintenance of trust

This principle received high scores in the PAT survey.

The focus groups all made reference to the need for trust – and also for the time needed to develop trust.

At an organisational level, it seemed clear that recent successes have started the process of building trust. The challenge would be to deliver enough success to outweigh long memories of perceived insults or out-smartings. In the detailed notes of the March workshop, no less than four out of the eight focus groups made reference to the innately competitive behaviour of medical staff. One group laid down a challenge to their medical colleagues to prove that they could be 'excellent in partnership', and 'build bridges, rather than put up barricades'.

Principle 5: Clear and robust partnership arrangements

This area of the partnership scored a mean 15.7 in the survey, putting it within the category of 'partnership arrangements are reasonably clear and robust'. There are many references in the literature to the need for clear goals, milestones and control mechanisms (eg Walters et al 1994; Birnbirg 1998; Morgan 1977; Hackett 1996; Schaafsma 1997).

The partnership had sought to put some of this into place but clearly more work needed to be done. The internal stakeholder focus group referred to a need for shared performance indicators, related to overall performance and to the partnership.

Principle 6: Monitoring, measuring and learning

This principle required agreement on a range of success criteria with clear arrangements for monitoring both the partnerships service aims and objectives, and the partnership itself. A mean score in the audit of 15.7 indicates a reasonable performance but leaves room for improvement.

A key message which came out from the internal stakeholder discussions was the need to value and reward good practice and performance – and to have shared information and shared performance indicators. Staff at all levels have been keen to promote the concept of learning from good practice and from mistakes. The latter has generated much debate. Does the best learning come from those things which do not go right, or in an NHS that is blame-focused and intolerant of failure, is it best to cover up those things which are not successful?

Culture

A question which remained was whether the cultures of the two organisations was compatible with a partnership model. The behaviour of individuals in the organisations is driven by the beliefs, values and norms which make up the corporate culture, which has been developed over a long period and is enshrined in the rites and rituals of organisational life. Both hospitals were large organisations which might be expected to have within them a number of sub-cultures, each with their own characteristics.

There was evidence from the focus groups and from the interviews that the cultures of the two hospitals were perceived as being different. If values are the driving force which determines behaviour and given the complexity of sub-cultures across the two hospitals, then achieving a 'blended culture' as described by Walters et al (1994) may be impossible. Rather, it would be better to aspire to the concept of 'unity and diversity' described by Klagge (1995) and try to retain the uniqueness of each culture, recognising that over time, if all the other component parts of a successful partnership are in place, then behaviours will move closer together.

The survey suggested that the need for the partnership was understood and that there was commitment to developing a successful partnership. It seemed that if all the characteristics which enable success were put into place, there was no reason why the partnership should not succeed.

Conclusions

It is curious that within the health sector, whilst recognising the need for greater collaboration across sectoral boundaries, and across primary, secondary and tertiary care, there has been a rush to merge rather than form partnerships. Does structural change in the form of 'merger mania' represent a lack of understanding of the issues and opportunities of partnership – or does it represent a realistic appraisal of the incompatibility of the long-term nature of partnership with short term political gain requirements? It must be said that few mergers can point to success yet, pre-occupied as they are with process and structure.

Some internal and external stakeholders saw this partnership at an early stage as a pre-cursor to a painless merger in the future. Others, perhaps the majority of senior clinicians and managers, and perhaps instinctively rather than evidence-based, saw the partnership as being the long-term future which will deliver benefits without the inertia and trauma of a merger process. At the time of writing (September 2001) the partnership continues to develop. There is now an agreed strategy for acute services to which the Trusts are committed, and a strategy for the health community. There is evidence of service transfers and support for capital developments to achieve the strategy.

References

Birnbirg, J.G. (1998) 'Control in Interfirm Co-operative Relationships' *Journal of Management Studies* 35:4.

Cravens, D.W., Shipp, S.H., Cravens, K.S. (1993) 'Analysis of Co-operative Inter-Organisational Relationships, Strategic Alliance Formation and Strategic Alliance Effectiveness' *Journal of Strategic Marketing* no 1 pp. 55–70.

Dyer, J.H, Kale, P. and Singh, H. (2001) 'How To Make Strategic Alliances Work' *MIT Sloan Management Review* 42:4 pp. 37–43.

Goddard, M. and Mannion, R. (1998) 'From Competition to Co-operation: New Economic Relationships in the National Health Service' *Health Economics* Vol. 7 pp. 105–119.

Hackett, M.C. (1996) 'Are there Alternatives to Merger?' *Health Manpower Management* 22:5.

HSC (1997) *The New NHS: Modern, Dependable*, HMSO.

Hardy, B., Hudson, B. and Waddington, E. (2000) 'What Makes a Good Partnership? A Partnership Assessment Tool' Nuffield Institute, Leeds University & NHS Executive Trent.

Klagge, J. (1995) 'Unity and Diversity' *Leadership & Organization Development Journal* 16:4.

Morgan, G. (1977) *Images of Organization*, Sage.

Newchurch (1998) 'Approaches to Implementing Strategic Change Reconfiguring Services: Testing the Benefits of Trust Mergers' Newchurch & Company Ltd.

Schaafsma, H. (1997) 'A Networking Model of Change for Middle Managers' *Leadership & Organization Development Journal* 18:1.

THS 1998 'Planning Your Merger for Long Term Success' Times Health Supplement, June.

Walters, B.A., Peters, S. and Dess, G.G. (1994) 'Strategic Alliances and Joint Ventures: Making Them Work' *Business Horizons* July/August.

■ Since May 2000, Thelma Holland has been Chief Executive of the Cornwall & Isles of Scilly Health Authority. She started her NHS career in nursing and health visiting, working in both the acute and community sectors. She has been a Director of Community Nursing and Learning Disability, a Change Management Consultant with the NHS Training Authority, a Senior Research Fellow at the Centre for Health Planning and Management at the University of Keele, a Unit General Manager, a Chief Executive of an NHS Trust. Her hobbies include sailing, walking and amateur theatre.

CHAPTER SEVEN

Team working in primary care

Lynda Hanson

Introduction

The many changes presently facing the National Health Service place a premium on the adaptability of organisations, and the ability of staff to respond to change will be an important stabilising factor within the NHS, and a key element in delivering the government aim of an equitable, patient focused, cost effective and accountable service.

The New World, New Opportunities Report (1993) recommended the team approach to health care delivery, and described primary health care team working as an appropriate structure to deliver its objectives through:

- establishing shared vision and objectives;
- deploying and developing skills appropriate to the identified health needs of the population;
- teams as the best platform for achieving the best clinical outcomes and service innovation.

Within my own organisation, Calderdale Healthcare NHS Trust, a decision was taken to remove a tier of management in community nursing, and invest the monies saved in the primary health care teams. Power was devolved to these primary health care teams in terms of budgetary control, recruitment and selection and skill mix issues. Originally there were 23 Primary Health Care Teams, consisting of between 15–20 members of staff including health visitors, health care assistants and district nurses, the majority of staff being district nursing staff.

I carried out a small piece of research in the light of this structural change, to establish whether the new structure had provided the correct nurturing/supportive environment to enable effective team working. This chapter summarises some of this research.

Structure and culture

The links between structure and culture are strong. Structure can be thought of in terms of the skeleton of the anatomy of an organisation, when perhaps culture can be regarded as the physiology.

Several typologies of organisational culture have been developed (eg Deal and Kennedy 1982; Quinn and McGrath 1985; Goffee and Jones 1998). One of the earliest and most enduring is that of Roger Harrison (1972), who classified an organisation's culture against four different categories – power, role, task and self. Harrison's work was modified by Handy (1993) and it has become one of the most common models of organisational culture.

As a first exercise in investigating the primary health care teams, I used a questionnaire based on a design by Harrison, which asked team members a series of questions about values and behaviours. The questionnaire was used to discover:

1. The kind of culture – defined in terms of power, role, task or person – the respondents would prefer
2. The kind of culture they perceived to exist in their health care team
3. The kind of culture they perceived to exist in the Trust as a whole

A brief summary of the characteristics of the four cultures is:

- A Power culture is characterised by a single power source which spreads throughout the organisation: resource power and charisma are the main bases for the exercise of authority.
- A Role culture typically accompanies bureaucracy and hierarchical structures: this is the culture we might expect for an organisation such as an NHS trust.
- A Task culture is basically a team culture and the accent is on flexibility and mutual respect, and work is seen as the common enemy.
- A Person culture is developed when a group of people decide on a collective, self-orientated approach rather than an individual one.

Table 1: Preferred and actual organisational cultures

Rank	Individual preference	Culture of team	Culture of Trust
1st	Task	Task	Role
2nd	Person	Person	Task
3rd	Role	Role	Power
4th	Power	Power	Person

I sent the questionnaire to 22 team co-ordinators in the four localities across the district, plus the management team links, a total of 25 questionnaires. Nineteen questionnaires were returned. The results are summarised in Table 1

Four out of the five groups said task culture was predominant in their team (the fifth said the dominant culture was person-orientated).

The results show that the preferred individual culture generally aligned with that of the service team, whereas that of the organisation as a whole differed from individual preferences (three of the organisations were perceived as having strong role cultures).

This indicated to me that the service management team was providing a helpful cultural environment for its members, aligning with their own individual preferences.

Improvements through the primary health care teams

As the next step in my inquiry, I carried out eight semi-structured interviews with four team co-ordinators and four GPs, in each of the four district localities.

Pearson and Spencer (1995) utilised a two stage Delphi questionnaire to determine agreed indicators of effective team work in primary care. Responses from 137 people involved in primary care work rated the importance of twenty indicators. The four most significant indicators were

- agreed aims, goals, objectives;
- effective communication;
- patients receiving the best possible care;
- individual roles defined and understood.

With these points in mind, in the interviews I explored:

- Whether flattened structures result in improved team working – through democratic decision making and improved communication;
- Whether primary health care teams provide an effective model of working;
- The extent to which teams require time to evolve and develop through differing stages;
- Whether shared values and culture are important to support effective team working.

The responses in this first area of inquiry – whether flattened structures result in improved team working – are summarised in Table 2.

Table 2: A flattened structure results in improved team working

Subject	Mentioned by GP				Mentioned by co-ordinator				Total
	loc.1	loc.2	loc3	loc.4	loc.1	loc.2	loc.3	loc.4	
1. Improved communication									
a) overall	✓	✓	✓		✓		✓	✓	6
b) specifically with the trust	✓	✓	✓		✓		✓	✓	6
c) with GPs	✓	✓	✓	✓	✓	✓	✓	✓	8
2. Improved working environment/organisation		✓	✓		✓		✓	✓	5
3. Less dictatorial working framework	✓	✓		✓	✓	✓	✓	✓	7
4. Improved team working	✓	✓	✓	✓		✓	✓	✓	7
5. Increased understanding of each other's role			✓			✓			2
6. Enabled democratic decision-making	✓	✓			✓	✓	✓		5
7. Allowed shared ownership	✓						✓		2
8. Individuals/teams better informed					✓		✓	✓	3
9. Enabled change	✓	✓	✓	✓	✓	✓	✓	✓	8
10. Devolved management	✓	✓	✓	✓	✓	✓			6

loc. = Locality

Improved communication was seen as an important factor by all interviewees. Specifically highlighted was the improved communication between the team members and the GPs.

> We've certainly felt close to the centre of things with the structure the way it is now; no two ways about that. Everybody said the same. We felt better informed this last 18 months than ever before and we felt that's been a real two way thing.
>
> Team Co-ordinator

> We feel we are working together as a team and pushing things forward with the suggestions from the practice and from the nurses as well and we feel that the flattened management structure has actually enhanced that process, where the old management structure put a barrier between the two of us really.
>
> GP

> I know there was one meeting where there was some conflict going on and differing agendas were coming out, but afterwards the GP actually came back to me and explained why he had reacted in that way. Now for me that was a big positive, because I wouldn't have had that, sort of 12, 18 months ago, but now I feel quite privileged. He's actually come to me at a later date to say – this is how I am feeling and this is why I've reacted in this way.
>
> Team Co-ordinator

Perceptions of improvement were not uniform. The GP in one locality, for example, said that communication was already good within the primary health care team, whereas the co-ordinator felt there had been an improvement in communication in all areas.

Improved working environment/organisation was seen as helpful by 2 out of 4 GPs and 3 out of 4 of the team co-ordinators.

> There aren't any secrets any more about management. It was always kept a bit of a mystery. ... we all felt that that's gone now and there isn't that great mystery surrounding anything any more.

> ... we talked about the bottom up approach and we definitely felt we were getting there with that.
>
> Team co-ordinator

This indicates how disempowering the previous hierarchical structure had been, and how power had been exerted through control of information.

Less dictatorial working framework was seen as being helpful by the 'flattened structure' by 7 out of the 8 interviewees.

> The communication's better. I personally think it less sort of dictatorial. When we had a manager we were told what to do; it wasn't a team decision.

> Communication's far better, far better. I think that's the main thing about it and there's no 'do as you're told' type of thing; its all democratic and a shared sort of ownership. Very much so, yes.
>
> Team co-ordinator

This links with the results of the questionnaire on culture. Handy (1990) describes the 'task culture' as one in which work is the common enemy and power is diffused, being based on expertise, rather than position or charisma.

Improved team working – seven out of ten felt the flattened structure improved team working and *all* the GPs felt this was the case.

> Well, I think it's enabled us to, certainly to communicate better between the district and health visitors and ourselves. I definitely think we've managed to organise things within the practice better as a result. In the past we found it difficult to actually find our manager to be honest, and she seemed fairly distant from what was going on within the practice. So on that, I think that's a fairly positive change.
>
> GP

Increased understanding of each other's role – only two out of eight commented that the flattened structure had increased the understanding of each other's roles. This is quite interesting as a key indicator of effective team working is an understanding of each other's roles. The response might be that actually team members think they already understand each other's roles? This is an area for further study.

> We've had two school nurses that would really like to be aligned to the team, because they have been so helpful for the GPs because they did not realise what the school nurses did; they thought they were 'nit nurses' so they came back and gave them (GPs) a really good overview

of their role … the GPs invited them back because they (the GPs) were having problems about sexual health in a certain school.

Team co-ordinator

This comment clearly demonstrates how, with a better understanding of each other's role, more effective team working will result.

Individuals/teams better informed – it was interesting to note that three out of the four team co-ordinators felt the teams were better informed, but this factor was not mentioned by any of the GPs.

We have monthly meetings and we all put into those meetings from the auxiliary up to the three GPs and they are always well attended, there are always 16 or 17 members of staff.

Team co-ordinator

Enabled change – all eight interviewed felt that the flattened structure had enabled change. In interviewing this was one of the most animated perspectives highlighted. Individuals were keen to outline changes which had been implemented.

I think we've certainly looked at a lot of working practices and changed the working practices.

Team co-ordinator

Interestingly one GP indicated that the 'change' was perhaps in the fact that the team could *now openly demonstrate the working together as a team* rather that not being able to tell the trust management exactly what was being undertaken because of the previous lines of demarcation and the fear of trust staff.

Responses to the second area of inquiry – the extent to which primary health care teams provide an effective model of working – are summarised in Table 3.

Utilises resources better, financial/human – interestingly only one team co-ordinator mentioned efficient usage of budget which was surprising, since all the co-ordinators hold devolved budgets. Budget issues were not mentioned by any of the GPs. However, all the GPs felt 'people' and their talents/competencies are utilised more effectively as did three out of four team co-ordinators.

Table 3: Primary health care teams provide an effective model of working

Subject	Mentioned by GP				Mentioned by co-ordinator				Total
	loc.1	loc.2	loc3	loc.4	loc.1	loc.2	loc.3	loc.4	
1. Utilise resources better									
a) Budget					✓				1
b) Human resources	✓	✓	✓	✓	✓	✓	✓	✓	8
2. Allows patient centred care	✓	✓	✓	✓		✓	✓	✓	7
3. Allows 'blurring of roles'	✓	✓	✓	✓			✓	✓	6
4. Sharing experience/ learning environment	✓	✓	✓				✓	✓	5

Patient-centred approach – there was a strong response on the ability of the primary health care team to provide a patient centred approach, with six out of eight interviewees commenting.

> I think all of this comes down to one of my hobby horses, which is patient centred care – I feel that it's more sensitive to the needs of the patient.
>
> GP

This also fits with information provided by reviews conducted by Huddersfield University and a review undertaken by the Nuffield Institute on district nursing, school nursing and health visiting and is perhaps the key motivating factor in that members of the team see themselves as the professionals providing essential services to those in need, with a high level of satisfaction.

Blurring of roles – five out of eight interviewees comment on the 'blurring' of roles (three out of four GPs and 2 out of 4 co-ordinators). The blurring of roles and understanding of roles is a key element in the effectiveness of team working, according to West (1996).

> We're making much more use of the auxiliary, she actually does screening for instance, in diabetic clinics.
>
> Another example is the nursery nurse, doing her baby massage for colicky children which has proven a big, big positive thing.
>
> GP

Sharing experience/learning environment – four out of eight felt the primary health care team's ability to share experience delivered a more efficient way of working.

These comments are in line with the ideas in New World, New Opportunities (1993) about deploying and developing skills appropriate to the identified health needs of the population, and about teams being the best platform for achieving the best clinical outcomes and service innovation.

In the third area of inquiry – exploring team development issues – there were many more responses by co-ordinators than by GPs. All the co-ordinators had experienced opposition to change, for example, but perhaps this is not surprising as it was the co-ordinators who had undergone major change in working practice.

> Being nurses, they [the team members] were used to a hierarchical structure and they were all used to being told what to do and I think to be empowered and have a team co-ordinator who is not a manager, who is saying to them – Well, this is what we have to do. How are we going to do it? And you are going to be part of this. It's been very, very threatening. We've had all the displays of, you know, sort of conflict.
>
> Team co-ordinator

The 'traditional' nurse is exhibiting the classic symptoms of stress in the midst of change – a sense of mistrust and fear. Hand (1995) also describes the problems of getting people to assume greater responsibility and that it's not easy. Management *support* rather than control is required and people, for their part, need to learn to take responsibility.

In the fourth area of inquiry – on the extent to which respondents thought shared values and culture were important to support effective team working, seven interviewees mentioned 'true involvement of all players', an equality issue.

> So I think the important thing with teams before you start moving forward is getting everybody on board and everyone involved in the process so everybody feels a part of it and not just the team leader saying this, that and the other, bit I feel the team has evolved in – it's a long way down that line, quite honestly.
>
> GP

Five interviewees mentioned feeling valued

> She thinks it's wonderful because she is asked her opinion, she's invited to the meetings.

Team co-ordinator Locality 3

Other aspects of shared values and culture that were mentioned included honesty and trust

> We find that we can be very honest and open across all of us now. I mean Dr – has kept us well informed from the GP side with the BCGs.

Team co-ordinator

Only one person commented on shared objectives and the need for strategic planning. This is an area of concern considering that the setting of team objectives and having a shared vision is one of the major priorities in terms of team building (West 1994 and Pearson and Spencer 1995). If the teams are to be developed, further work and facilitation will be required to give them support in setting annual and long term objectives.

Other issues volunteered by respondents, when they were given the opportunity to add any further comments, were commitment and autonomy.

> [Previously] the team was stressed and there was a high level of sickness and all this and that and I think that's one of the things that's easily measurable. That's more or less been swept away. We don't have the long-standing sickness we used to have.

GP

This comment was confirmed by the human resources department. Since the introduction of self managed teams the sickness/absence rate had dropped dramatically.

> …particularly when we had those two terminal children last year, the huge amount of work that the community nurses took on board for that was phenomenal and that was stuff that we knew very little about because it was out at the paediatric oncology place at XX. But they really took to it and I honestly feel five years ago these children would have died in hospital. There is no way, I mean even with the liaison

nurses, who were superb, it was the groundwork of the district nurses that were prepared to work long hours over the weekend that made it possible, you know, just those two cases highlighted how well the team worked.

GP

We're much more willing for nurses to take a lead in looking after patients and also they're willing to take on this role where we can be an advisory thing, whereas in the old days a doctor would go, a nurse would go, and then another nurse and then another doctor or whatever.

GP

...a lot of the time, the nurses themselves, were taking initiatives. It wasn't, well, would you do this, would you do that, they were going, I'll do that, I'll do that.

GP

The increased autonomy of the team. We can make decisions about the way of working and do it. Which is nice!

Team co-ordinator

Conclusions

Following the introduction of self managed teams and restructuring, the culture of the service team matched that of the individuals' preferences for a task culture – a team culture in which work is the common enemy.

All interviewees expressed support for team working and said that structural change had enabled team working to take place – this message was particularly strong from the GPs. There was a strong sense of improved motivation and expressions of reward and achievement in providing patient care.

Findings from the interviews indicated there had been real change in working practices, with more effective usage of staff and more scope for them to develop their roles. Teams are utilising skill mix and innovative ways of working through their decision-making powers to maximise both human and financial resources.

In terms of Pearson and Spencer's (1995) indicators of effective team working:

- Agreed aims, goals and objectives
the aims of improving care seemed to be accepted by all teams, although only one team out of four mentioned objectives.

- Effective communication
was highlighted by all respondents as having improved.

- Patients receiving best possible care
there was from all the teams an overwhelming desire to improve patient care (together) and push the barriers back in terms of innovative ways of delivering patient care.

- Individual roles defined and understood
only one GP but three out of four team co-ordinators felt that clarity of roles had been experienced.

On the evidence of this study, the use of self managed teams in the acute sector could lead to reduced sickness and absence levels and a more motivated workforce.

Postscript

Handy (1990) describes the task culture as the most difficult to keep working effectively. Hammer and Champy (1996) also remark that with a flattened structure people have to work much harder to network and to work effectively. The support factor is recognised as the key or the 'glue' which holds the system together. The service management team worked hard in the early stages to ensure financial, human resources and professional support to the team co-ordinators was consistently available, along with capacity for team time-outs and cross networking.

Three years on, and the initial intensive support in terms of general management, HR, finance and professional leadership to the teams has gradually reduced. The Primary Health Care Teams are functioning well and are demonstrating total self-sufficiency. The teams have been involved and are pro-active in meeting the challenges of Primary Care Trust development and the demands of the modernisation agenda. They have recently undertaken a Community Nursing Review and have been particularly key in setting the Clinical Governance agenda alongside GP colleagues. Development has taken place not only of the teams but also of individuals in areas such as clinical effectiveness. The GPs continue to be impressed by the development not only of their own teams but also by the improvements across the whole district.

The teams have delivered on their objectives, have remained within budget and have attracted staff into the district: out of a staff of 264 community personnel we have sustained a position of zero vacancies since December 1998, despite the national picture of nursing shortages. One of the key elements of the teams' success is the ability to provide quick and effective working solutions to problems which, with traditional management structures, would remain unresolved for a much longer period of time. The skill mix has changed for each individual team over a period of time and it's interesting to note that some teams have actually skilled up in terms of percentage of qualified nursing hours and other teams have actually skilled down, using more health care assistants because it is appropriate to their particular working environment.

At the same time as the introduction of the Primary Health Care Teams, using a whole systems approach, we introduced Rehabilitation Teams working on a multi-professional basis across the district. Joint Mental Health Teams were also developed with our Local Authority partners. Additionally a building/estates programme was rolled out for community in alignment with the acute PFI hospital build (hand over April 2001). The whole systems approach has in fact supported the development of the Primary Health Care Team and enabled the meeting the NHS Plan agenda in terms of intermediate care and primary care development.

References

Deal, T.E. & Kennedy, A.A. (1982) *Corporate Cultures: The Rites and Rituals of Corporate Life* Mass: Addison-Wesley.

Goffee, R. and Jones, G. (1998) *The Character of a Corporation*, London: HarperCollins.

Hammer, M. Champy, J. (1996) *Re-Engineering the Corporation: A Manifesto for Business Revolution,* London: Nicholas Brearley Publications.

Hand, M. (1995) Empowerment – You Can't Give It, People Have to Want It *Management Development Review. Vol. 8 No. 3* pp 36–40.

Handy, C. (1990) *Inside Organisations* London: BBC Publications.

Handy, C. (1993) *Understanding Organisations* Harmondsworth: Penguin.

Harrison, R. (1972) Understanding Your Organisation's Character *Harvard Business Review* 50 May–June 119–28.

NHS Management Executive (1993) *New World, New Opportunities* London: HMSO.

Pearson, P. & Spencer, J. (1995) 'Pointers to effective teamwork: exploring primary care'. *Journal of Interprofessional Care*, 9(2), 131–8.

Quinn, R. E. & McGrath, M.R. (1985) The Transformation of Organisational Cultures: A Competing Values Perspective; *Organisational Culture* 315–34.

West, M. (1994) Effective Teamwork *British Psychological Society* Leicester.

■ Lynda Hanson is the Director of Operations and Facilities at Calderdale and Huddersfield NHS Trust. She originally trained and qualified as a Radiographer at Bradford. Having progressed to the post of District Imaging Services Manager for Calderdale, she then applied and was successful in achieving the post of Service Manager for Family/Community for Calderdale Trust (when this research took place).

CHAPTER EIGHT

Multi-disciplinary team working and participative empowerment

Judith Holbrey

I was appointed in January 1997 as Director of Corporate Development & Nursing of a National Health Service Trust that provided a comprehensive range of hospital and community services.

A decision had been taken to centralise hospital services onto one site with an associated reduction in bed capacity. Benchmarking exercises had shown the Trust to be high in cost and low in productivity, whilst a management cost reduction had led to downsizing and de-layering. The Trust had commenced a major change project to examine all aspects of service delivery, with the objective of delivering clinically effective care, which was resource and cost efficient, whilst meeting the needs of all stakeholders including patients and staff.

One of my key responsibilities was to lead organisational development and change strategies. I established a change programme, which built on communication strategies, multi-disciplinary teamworking and approaches to business process re-engineering. I adapted the 'Transforming the Social Business' change methodology (Newchurch 1996) as the framework on which to achieve the change required. Two of the key requirements of this methodology are (Newchurch, 1996):

- Involvement in the project from all levels of the organisation, particularly those who will be most affected by the changes.
- A desire to change to benefit the end user of the service – ie the patient.

I thought that to meet these requirements the Trust needed to change from a hierarchical, control-focused organisation to one which better utilised the contribution of groups and teams.

In reaching this conclusion, I was influenced both by my own experience and by a number of key ideas on organisational development around participation, empowerment and the learning organisation.

A learning organisation accomplishes a '… high proportion of its productive changes through participation …' (Moss Kanter, 1995, p241) and success or failure of an organisation is '… fundamentally dependent on its people and how they are used…' (Bennis et al, 1995, p115).

Principles of adult learning are the foundations of the learning organisation: people will learn best when they need to solve meaningful problems (Schon 1983; Knowles 1984). Given the conditions to pursue their own way to solve a problem without a rigid framework it is suggested that adult and group learning will achieve the desired organisational transformation.

To manage this, a 'learning environment', both in the group and in the wider organisation, needs to be developed. Pedler et al (1991) identify this as one which encourages experiments, learns from mistakes and questions ideas, actions and attitudes.

In designing my organisational change programme one of the key principles I wanted to incorporate was one of 'ownership'. O'Connor (1993) describes the process of 'creating ownership' as letting those who are delegated responsibility help determine what a job should include and how this can be best achieved. Commitment by senior managers to delegation of control and local autonomy, and acceptance of responsibility by individuals and groups, are central to a successful learning organisation.

This is another way of describing empowerment – encouraging and allowing people to take responsibility for improving the way they do their jobs and contribute to the organisation's goals. (Carver in Clutterbuck, 1995, p12).

Thus participation and empowerment are inextricably linked and in my view 'participative empowerment' was the underpinning principle of the way I could change the organisation.

I decided to set up and to closely study a pilot change project in order to understand how best to move forward.

The pilot project was located in a paediatric outpatient clinic, where a number of problems had been identified relating to appointment systems and non-attendance by patients. I established a project team of staff involved in the clinic: a consultant paediatrician, a medical records manager, a staff nurse, a medical records clerk and two nursing auxiliaries.

None of the participants had any previous experience of project working. Afterwards the consultant and the clerical officer made particular reference to not having previously experienced working in multi-disciplinary groups that 'involved everyone'.

A first priority was to determine the parameters and ground rules. I believed without structure, groups can flounder unproductively. As Moss Kanter says, the fewer the constraints the more time the group will spend on defining its structure rather tackling the task (1995, p248). The sense of purpose and direction for a multi-disciplinary team is of prime importance. Briner et al (1994) consider that every project needs a 'big picture' from which everyone can see what the project is and why it is important.

The pre-project briefing included two key points:

1. This was an opportunity for the team to 'solve' the identified problem and achieve improvement. It was stressed that there would be no measurement of 'failure' and that the desired outcome would be determined by the team.
2. My vision for organisational empowerment, and my belief that experiences and lessons learnt would help a 'roll out' programme to develop other 'service improvement' teams.

Each member of staff was given the opportunity not to participate – but they all decided to take part. I arranged for the release of staff from other duties to be able to attend project team meetings.

To support the project, I appointed an experienced facilitator not previously known to the team.

A common failure in change programmes is to identify the project or task to be achieved by a team and then say they are empowered. Without a facilitator the reverse can happen and feelings of disempowerment and failure may occur. The role of facilitator is to hold the context so that all participants 'suspend their assumptions' (Bohm, in Senge, 1993, p243). The result '... brings to the surface the full depth of people's experience and thought, and yet can move beyond their individual views...' (Senge, 1993, p241). This is the basis for productive dialogue that supports learning in the team. A good facilitator ensures that dialogue is kept moving and is purposeful.

The facilitator used the 'skilled helper' model developed by Egan (1993) to structure the decision making process in the team.

The skilled helper model has three key stages. Stage 1 assesses the *current scenario,* to identify current problems and challenges and what is happening. Stage 2 develops the *preferred scenario,* to assess what things would look like if they looked better. Stage 3 develops *action strategies* which are identified and agreed by the group but may be taken forward individually or as task sub-groups and may involve other stakeholders.

The project lasted twelve weeks, from the initial briefing to carrying out the necessary changes. The outcome was very successful with a 50% reduction in the DNA (Did Not Attend) rate.

One of the potential obstacles to team learning can be conflicts and barriers between members of the team.

The Trust is a complex and varied organisation of professions, disciplines and service teams, each with their own political and professional sensitivities. Organisational boundaries and hierarchies have developed and matured over many years to a culture and way of working which Moss Kanter (1995) describes as 'segmentalist'.

In a segmentalist organisation innovation is inhibited through 'specialist biases' and 'political conflicts'. Resistance to change and desire for stability is supported by hierarchical and position power. Thus the involvement of those who might perceive their power base as being challenged – for example, consultants – is critical.

The barriers of segmentalism can sometimes be removed by moving people out of the boxes of hierarchy into integrative structures which foster innovation. This can be achieved through the temporary task structures of multi-disciplinary project teams, where team members 'view each other as colleagues in a mutual quest for deeper insight and clarity.' (Senge, 1993, p245). But traditional barriers may be replicated within the membership of the team: as Moss Kanter (1995) points out, teams that comprise members with different external statuses '... may slip into deference patterns ...which give those with higher status ... a more privileged position ...'(Moss Kanter, 1995, p256). If these barriers are not recognised and understood, it can inhibit the desired participation and change.

At the end of the project I carried out an interview with each member of the team. Each interview lasted half an hour and all were held within a 48 hour timescale.

I analysed the interview data using the framework developed by the Social and Community Planning Social Research Unit (Ritchie & Spencer, 1994), and drew out key themes from what was said.

Whilst acknowledging that these are initial findings of exploratory work, and that other groups with different membership and personalities may not present the same experience, 1 believe the findings are no less valid and that issues raised in this study can be addressed through recognition of potential pitfalls and by replicating those factors which positively contributed to the project.

It was clear that, through involvement in the project, relationships and understanding developed and improved. Participants became more tolerant of problems and, more importantly, displayed a willingness to solve problems beyond the project area. All participants had developed more understanding of what caused difficulties in the project area. This led to more realistic expectations that reduced frustration but also allowed action to address contributing factors.

The involvement of a facilitator and the use of Egan's (1993) Skilled Helper Model were crucial in creating shared vision and ownership. Five participants felt that the facilitator maintained the focus for the group. Four mentioned the facilitator's role in managing relationships and making the group feel relaxed. Three participants said that the group would not have identified all issues without a facilitator. The excitement and 'fun' generated by identifying the 'ideal' future scenario (from Stage 2 of the Egan model) when harnessed to the agreement of targets and the allocation of tasks to members appears to have been fundamental in overcoming potential difficulties in terms of hierarchy and conflict about responsibility for perceived problems.

Four participants considered that a facilitator was key to future projects. One said '... the most important message would be to get yourself a good facilitator ...'

Involvement in the project clearly did not equalise power, with evidence that position and hierarchy outside the group was replicated in group meetings and working relationships. Interestingly, only the consultant who had the most position power viewed this as a potential difficulty for others, none of whom raised it as an issue. Instead, working to benefit the consultant was expressed as a reason for involvement in the project and did not present difficulties for more junior staff. The danger of 'deference patterns' of behaviour (Moss Kanter, 1995) appeared in this case to be offset by the 'dialogue' between members who viewed themselves as colleagues with a shared vision and goal.

However, the consultant said that many of her consultant colleagues would find it difficult to work as an equal and not use their positional power. One other group member said that although the group had not been handpicked it was an easier group because the consultant is: '... quite laid back and can actually come down to our level...'

Thus a group can act in pursuit of a common purpose and goal, but does not need to modify hierarchy to equalise power. This enables the change programme to progress within existing culture and control systems without threat or challenge to those in positions of power although possibly at the expense of achieving empowerment.

Views on leadership of the project raised interesting issues. The consultant and two managers viewed myself as leader or external stakeholder whereas, despite the same briefing, the nursing staff considered the Health Records Administration Manager as group leader with the power and ability to make things happen. Again this is an issue of hierarchy and does not appear to necessitate action or modification to the change programme suggesting that there is acknowledged flexibility and scope for different leaders providing they share the overall vision.

The project highlighted how far participation in the project achieved empowerment and increased responsibility. Although there had been clearly identified problems in the paediatric outpatient clinic prior to commencement of the project, none of the participants had felt they had either the ability or responsibility to effect change. At the end of the project participants recognised that they had a contribution to make once a project was identified – but involvement does not appear to have empowered individuals or the group to take responsibility for identifying the need for change or for implementing change in their own working area. Conversely, however, there was a demonstration of a strong inclination to be involved in any future projects alongside recognition of the value of using a similar approach elsewhere. This raises doubts about participation being the basis of empowerment, suggesting that multidisciplinary team working achieves involvement without responsibility or ownership. The missing element is the motivation to initiate and implement continued improvement. If this is the case, does it matter and if so how should it be addressed?

One solution lies in creating a 'demand-pull' change programme. Daniels (1994) differentiates between the *supply-push* change programme approach whereby managers are 'pushed' into giving up control and team members are pushed into sharing responsibility and the *demand-pull* approach where, through providing structure and parameters, teams develop confidence, becoming more self directing with more power and freedom. Rewards provide the motivation for the team and a cyclical process of reinforcement and feedback means that in *demand-pull* '… acceptance occurs faster and resistance is practically eliminated …' (Daniels, 1994, p137).

Demand-pull requires leaders to not let achievement of project objectives became the end point but instead to encourage the start of a new way of working. The pilot project group was evidencing signs of wanting to continue working to improve the paediatric clinic, but as the interviews were undertaken shortly after project completion there was no experience within the group of feeling empowered. Whether the onus lies with the leader or the participants it is important to make the work of the group more visible to promote commitment and motivation.

The practical arrangements and supporting factors for future multidisciplinary team projects are summarised in Figure 1.

An important aspect is the need to involve the right people in the project. Participants in this project other than the staff nurse were chosen because they worked in the area. This became a motivator because they were able to influence and improve the area of work for the benefit of themselves, their patients or the organisation. The staff nurse by contrast experienced difficulties, recognised by others, which could potentially have led to making the group dysfunctional. This led me to the conclusion that future project team membership should draw on those people involved in the work area or who have a relevant contribution and not 'add in' extras for the sake of numbers or staff development.

Identifying a group leader is another important factor, for example in arranging meetings which are planned to suit all members with agreed start and finish times. Not to do so creates tension particularly for those staff who have competing and conflicting demands on their time. In particular this requires consideration by nurse managers as all three nurse participants had either to attend meetings in their own time or miss meetings because of not being released from other duties. This contrasts with

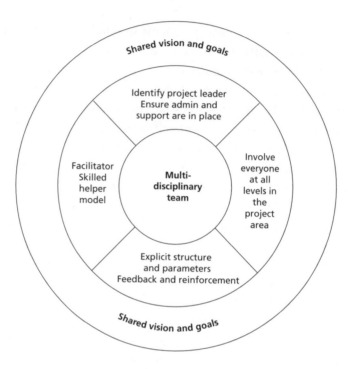

Figure 1: Support strategies for multi-disciplinary team working

the consultant and managers who more readily incorporated the project work and meetings into their other commitments.

Application

Following the completion of this study, and the favourable reactions towards the use of a facilitator I decided to use the lessons learnt to support the development needs of the organisation. I wanted to use facilitated, multi-disciplinary working groups and focus groups to a greater extent to deliver the organisational change programme.

The first and perhaps most important element of this strategy was to identify a team of facilitators who would be available to support these working groups. I worked with local university college to develop a three-day facilitation skills training programme, plus a support network for the facilitators. The intensive training programme provided both theoretical and practical based skills and used the Egan model as the framework.

The opportunity to become a facilitator was through self-selection following internal advertisement. The first cohort of 12 participants included a wide range of backgrounds including therapists, nurses, finance and human resource staff. This was so successful and popular that a further three cohorts were arranged in quick succession giving the Trust a 'pool' of facilitators who were also enthusiastic leaders of change strategies. In time the facilitator team included the Chairman of the Trust and was extended to staff from the local Community Health Council to help in working with groups of patients and users of the services provided by the Trust. An important element of the success of the facilitator approach was that each cohort had ongoing support through action learning set meetings.

The next element of the strategy was to publicise the availability of the facilitated approach. In the first instance this was closely managed by myself and was a high priority for the Directors of the Trust who were encouraged to identify project sponsors and projects that needed facilitation. Although there was general support, there was also some initial difficulty, and we needed to persevere and to persuade sponsors until the organisation developed confidence that change could be successfully managed in this way. Through the success of the early projects eventually the facilitated approach became embedded in the organisation so that at 18 to 24 months after it was first introduced there were more projects to be facilitated than available facilitators.

In the early stages, after the introduction of the facilitated approach, evaluation was based on uptake and general feedback from project facilitators, project participants and project sponsors. However after two years I felt it was important to undertake formal evaluation and commissioned this from the Trust Clinical Effectiveness and Audit Department. They undertook this evaluation through the use of structured questionnaire and interview. The key findings from this study were:

- all parties who had taken part in facilitated change projects – the sponsors, the facilitators and the facilitated – felt that the process had been beneficial
- sponsors largely felt that the process had made reaching recommendations and implementing them easier

The study also showed some areas for improvement at that time:

- the need for more clarity about the roles of sponsor and facilitator in co-ordinating projects
- the need for better communication throughout the project – particularly at the beginning and the end of the projects – during initial discussions, and following the implementation of recommendations

Conclusion

The project described in the initial study demonstrates that, providing a common vision and goal are shared by members of a multi-disciplinary team, issues of hierarchy and motivation can be managed to the benefit of all involved and thus contribute to organisational objectives. The resultant improvement in relationships amongst team members and a positive project outcome enthused people as followers, ambassadors and supporters of change.

The value of the initial study cannot be underestimated. Not only was the successful outcome of the project be used to generate support base for a wider use of the facilitation approach, but it also allowed some misconceptions to be identified and managed, to ensure that later projects could be given the optimum environment for success. The projects that have followed gave opportunities for people throughout the Trust to contribute to changes that affected them, and helped individuals and teams to feel empowered and have the ability to make improvements: in my opinion, these are key characteristics of learning organisation.

Bibliography

Bennis, W., Parikh, J. and Lessem, R., (1995) *Beyond Leadership*, Blackwell, Oxford.

Briner, W., Geddes, M. and Hastings, C. (1994) *Project Leadership*, Gower, Aldershot.

Clutterbuck, D. (1995) *The Power of Empowerment*, Kogan Page, London.

Daniels, A.C. (1994) *Bringing Out the Best in People*, McGraw-Hill, USA.

Egan, G. (1993) *Adding Value*, Jossey-Bass, San Francisco.

Knowles, M. (1984) *Self-Directed Learning*, Follett, Chicago.

Moss Kanter, R. (1995) *The Change Masters*, Routledge, London.

Newchurch (1996) 'Transforming the Social Business', Newchurch & Company Briefing Paper.

O'Connor, C.A. (1993) *The Handbook for Organizational Change*, McGraw-Hill, Maidenhead.

Pedler, M.J., Burgoyne, J.G. and Boydell, T.H. (1991) *The Learning Company*, McGraw-Hill, Maidenhead.

Ritchie, J. and Spencer, L. (1994) 'Qualitative Data Analysis for Applied Policy Research' in Bryman, A. and Burgess, R.G. (eds) *Analyzing Qualitative Data*, Routledge, London.

Schon, D. (1983) *The Reflective Practitioner*, Gower, Aldershot.

Senge, P. (1993) *The Fifth Discipline*, Century Business, London.

■ Judith Holbrey currently works for the NHS Executive in the Northern and Yorkshire Region where she holds a Performance Management role. Prior to this she was the Director of Corporate Development and Nursing in a NHS Trust providing a comprehensive range of acute, community and Mental Health services. A nurse by background Judith has held a wide range of clinical and general managerial roles through which she has consistently endeavoured to involve and support staff in improving services to patients and users and to achieve desired outcomes.

CHAPTER NINE

Engaging clinicians in decision making to support Clinical Governance

Andrea Hopkins

'In white water, we are better off with a flexible raft and twelve alert eyes than with a wooden boat in which one captain 'up top' directs a galley of fettered rowers.'

McLagan and Nel (1995)

Introduction

'The New NHS, Modern Dependable' (1997) set out the Government's vision of a significantly overhauled NHS, representing both radical reform and a gradual evolution of the system. One of the key themes was a focus on quality, providing patients with the twin guarantees of consistency and responsiveness from their local health service. To deliver this objective the Government required every NHS Trust to embrace the concept of Clinical Governance, so that quality is at the core of the responsibilities of the organisation and the responsibilities of each individual professional. Under Clinical Governance, Chief Executives will carry ultimate responsibility for the quality of the services provided by their organisations.

According to Peter Senge (1990) it is unlikely any individual at the head of a complex organisation can control the quality of the service delivered. He or she is dependent on the activities of those who live at the point of service. To provide a quality service, healthcare organisations will need to develop a highly participative culture, in which clinicians and managers work in partnership, with the majority of decisions made at or close to the point of service delivery.

I was interested in identifying the factors that lead to the effective engagement of clinicians in decision making, which would support the implementation of Clinical Governance within my Trust. I studied the available literature. I made a visit to a health organisation in the United States which has been internationally recognised as representing good practice. And I set out to investigate the views of a range of clinical staff employed by my Trust about their level of involvement in organisational decision making.

My Trust at the time of this research was an NHS provider of community health care and priority (mental health, learning disability and forensic) services, serving a population of over 320,000, from 38 separate community-based sites.

The Trust employed over 2,000 staff of which 48% were employed directly in clinical practice; in addition the majority of managers at all levels had clinical backgrounds. The majority of clinical staff were nurses, but the Trust also employed psychologists, doctors and allied health professionals (including occupational therapists, speech therapists, podiatrists, and physiotherapists).

The Trust had at the core of its mission statement a commitment to partnership working and encouraging staff to share their views. It had established a range of formal and informal mechanisms to facilitate these processes, including a decentralised organisational structure, and eight Clinical Management Teams (CMTs) which were responsible for multidisciplinary input into service management and co-ordination, with a key focus on improving service quality.

Participative decision making

> 'There is no limit to the ability to contribute on the part of a properly selected, well trained, appropriately supported, and, above all, committed person. The only limitation is the attitude of management'
>
> Tom Peters (1988)

Since the early seventies there has been a growing recognition that organisational success cannot be brought about by a few key individuals at the top. As we move from an industrial age to a new era of information, the technology is available to inform decision making at all levels, therefore in today's fast moving customer-focused world, success according to Drucker (1989, 1995) is:

> 'dependent on the ability of the organisation to harness the collective genius of those who work within it'

Highly participative organisations engage employees at every level of decision making from the highly tactical, task-focused decisions, to the strategic 'power issues' which are often the decision making province of senior management. McLagan and Nel (1995) argue that participation does not mean involving all the people all the time, but ensuring different perspectives are represented in order to improve the quality of the decision and to enhance commitment to the outcome.

Manthey (1998) in discussing decision making within the healthcare context, puts forward four essential perspectives which should be represented in decision making: the patient perspective, the staff perspective, the cost perspective, and the global (ie strategic) perspective. The decision making process therefore requires a partnership between managers and clinicians as the different perspectives are rarely embodied in one or two people.

According to Peters (1988) and Hand (1995) the key to participative decision making lies with managers. Although some employees will be more enthusiastic than others about grasping opportunities to participate, it is the attitude and behaviour of managers that determines success. Peters identifies the need for a management paradigm in which the role of management is to facilitate, support, resource and enable those who deliver the service to utilise their knowledge and creativity.

Hand (1995) believes that full participation in decision making equates with empowerment. He suggests a sense of empowerment is the difference between someone just doing a job and doing it with enthusiasm, imagination and a passion to ensure the customer is satisfied.

The American experience

As part of my research for this project, I visited St Joseph's Hospital in Atlanta, Georgia, where I witnessed first hand a highly participative approach to staff involvement which has led to St Joseph's being recognised as one of only eight 'Magnet' hospitals in the USA – so called because of their ability to attract staff (Buchan 1997).

In the early 1980s St Joseph's was experiencing major staff recruitment problems, particularly amongst nurses, which almost brought about its closure. Tim Porter O'Grady was appointed to introduce a new model of management, which sought to give nurses more control over the service they provided.

Porter O'Grady introduced an accountability based model of decision making, termed 'shared governance' establishing both a structure and more importantly a culture which facilitated decentralised decision-making. The approach gives nurses the authority and autonomy to make decisions and implement them. It is based on a partnership between clinicians and managers, each as equal partners in the decision making process.

Porter O'Grady revolutionised the approach to nursing management at St Joseph's Hospital on the underlying premise that 'the professional nurse providing direct care should be intimately involved in making decisions about the delivery of that care'. Under shared governance accountability must always be located at the place where decisions are appropriately made (Porter O'Grady 1992, 1995). Shared governance is based on principles of partnership, equity, accountability and ownership (Porter O'Grady et al 1997). Equity involves a recognition that each role contributes in different ways, but that no role is more important than another. Equity and partnership therefore form the bedrock of an organisation committed to establishing a participative and empowering culture.

In recent years the concept of shared governance has been developed as a vehicle for integrating all the activities of an organisation, a whole systems approach which encompasses the interdisciplinary nature of a patient centred service model. Several healthcare providers in the USA have since introduced the whole systems approach and described their journey and experiences (Evans et al 1995). They emphasise the challenge this offers to all the stakeholders, and the support, information and development required to facilitate the process. The role of management, they suggest, becomes one of integrating, facilitating, co-ordinating and ensuring the structure works and is properly resourced, and that point of care decisions are not made in other places, as this only serves to undermine the process.

My visit to St Joseph's was an inspiration, stimulating my interest to investigate the degree to which clinicians felt involved in decision making within my own Trust.

The survey

The main part of my research study was a survey of a sample of 40 nurses employed in first line management roles within the Trust. The sample represented 66% of the managers in this position. First line nurse managers occupy a special position, at the interface between those who deliver hands on care and those who administer the system that supports them. They are perceived as the clinical leaders who are in direct contact with patients and clients, but have overall responsibility for the delivery of care within a defined area of practice.

Thirty-eight completed questionnaires were returned, a response rate of 95%.

Prior to the survey I carried out semi-structured interviews with eight senior members of staff – four clinicians and four managers. The Trust structure was at that time based on four divisions, each with a specific service focus and each led by a Divisional Manager, all of whom had a clinical background but who were no longer hands-on care providers. I interviewed all four Divisional Managers. I also interviewed four Chairs of the Clinical Management Teams (CMTs) – the structures created to provide multi-disciplinary input into service management and to improve service quality. Each committee chair was a practising senior clinician, in most cases a medical consultant.

In compiling the questionnaire for the nurse managers, I combined the themes that emerged from the interviews with issues identified in the literature and issues that I gathered from my visit to St Joseph's.

Findings

> 'To empower, managers have to trust that peoples' motivation is no different from their own. For their people to commit themselves to greater ownership of the work, they must be able to trust their managers and feel able to exercise initiative without fear of recrimination'.
>
> Hand (1995)

The results of the interviews with senior staff would fill a chapter on their own, but in this paper I will concentrate mainly on the findings from the survey of the first line nurse managers.

At the start of the questionnaire I tried to identify any gap between what the nurses expected and their actual experience of involvement in decision making. The nurses were asked to complete a five-point scale to indicate whether they agreed or disagreed with fourteen statements about partnership and participation. The five-point scale permitted those with a neutral view to express it, an approach supported by Oppenheim (1984) as preferable to increasing the likelihood of non-responders. First, the nurses were asked about their expectations and then about their experiences. For example, in question 1 they were asked to rate their agreement with the statement 'I expect my views and opinions to be listened to' and in question 2 they were asked to rate their agreement with the statement, 'In my experience as an employee, my views and opinions are listened to'.

For ease of comparing expectations and experience, the responses to both questions are combined in Table 1.

Perhaps not surprisingly, all the nurse managers strongly agreed or agreed that 7 out of the of 14 statements were legitimate expectations; 97% strongly agreed, agreed or had no particular view about 12 out of 13 statements, and only 1 person (3%) disagreed with the statement 'I expect staff who deliver the service to make most of the decisions about how the service is delivered'.

This suggests that the majority of nurses in first line management positions believed they had an important role to play in decision making particularly in relation to the service they provided, and an expectation they should have freedom to innovate and the resources and information required to operate effectively.

Their experiences as employees were, however, different. There was only one statement where expectation and experience were closely matched which was 'I am held accountable for the service I deliver'. The areas of greatest dissonance were:

- Only 32% believed they had the resources they needed, 45% disagreed or strongly disagreed with this statement
- Only 19% agreed or strongly agreed that 'staff who deliver the service make most of the decisions about how the service is delivered'. 42% disagreed.

Table 1: Expectations and experience as an employee

	As an employee, I expect… [In my experience as an employee…] Figures are percentages. 37 responses to this part of the questionnaire	Strongly agree	Agree	Neither agree nor disagree	Disagree	Strongly disagree
A1	My views and opinions listened to	73 [5]	27 [65]	[16]	[14]	
A2	Have the resources I need to do my job	78	19 [32]	3 [24]	[40]	[5]
A3	Held accountable for the service I deliver	68 [45]	30 [50]	3 [5]		
A4	Involved in decisions which impact on the service I deliver	78 [3]	19 [47]	3 [24]	[26]	
A5	Managers work in partnership with clinical staff	78 [5]	22 [43]	[27]	[22]	[3]
A6	Managers provide feedback on performance	73 [5]	27 [43]	[22]	[30]	
A7	Managers provide me with the information I need to do my job	65 [8]	35 [42]	[40]	[11]	
A8	Have confidence in the decision making process	73 [14]	27 [24]	[38]	[22]	[3]
A9	Mechanisms exist which facilitate the involvement of clinical staff in decision making	78 [3]	22 [42]	[37]	[16]	
A10	Have freedom to innovate in my role	61 [5]	36 [53]	3 [21]	[18]	[3]
A11	Staff who deliver the service make most of the decisions about how the service is delivered	46 [3]	49 [16]	3 [34]	[42]	
A12	Feel valued	86 [5]	11 [29]	3 [37]	[26]	[3]
A13	Have an appropriate level of authority to make changes which improve the service for patients	59 [52]	41 [47]	[29]	[16]	[3]
A14	Mutual trust exists between Clinicians and Senior Managers	81 [42]	16 [26]	3 [10]	[5]	

- 29% disagreed or strongly disagreed with the statement 'I feel valued' (but 34% agreed or strongly agreed with the statement).
- 30% disagreed that 'Managers provide feedback on performance' – however 48% agreed or strongly agreed with the statement.
- 25% disagreed or strongly disagreed with the statement 'I have confidence in the decision making process' – however 38% agreed or strongly agreed.

The range of opinions indicated differences in the experience of employees, which might indicate different styles and cultures in different sections of the organisation.

The data suggested that approximately 50% (20) of the nurses had a positive perspective in relation to their involvement and degree of empowerment, approximately 20–30% (8–11) were less committal, and the remaining 20% appear to have very negative perceptions of the Trust regarding their involvement and degree of empowerment.

In another question, respondents were asked how they rated the Trust's commitment to involving clinical staff in decision making. To what extent did they think that:

- Every effort is made to ensure there is a clinical perspective within the decision making process (50% strongly agreed or agreed)
- Decision making is appropriately devolved to those with the knowledge of the service (46% agreed)
- There is a genuine desire to empower clinicians to make service decisions (51% strongly agreed or agreed)
- Manager and Clinicians are encouraged to work together as equal partners (42% strongly agreed or agreed)
- Timely and accurate information to support decision making is readily available (35% strongly agreed or agreed)

Analysing the responses this question by service areas, I found that Community General nurses (15 respondents representing 40% of the overall total – a category which includes both District Nurses and Health Visitors) had an overall positive view of participation in the Trust, with between 9 and 11 of them strongly agreeing or agreeing with each statement. As the largest group represented in the sample this impression skewed the overall results.

Nurses working in Learning Disabilities (7 respondents), which included both hospital-based staff as well as those employed in community homes, were the second most positive group with 3 or 4 respondents strongly agreeing or agreeing with four of the five statements.

Most other service areas were noncommittal, with the majority of responses falling in the middle column. One service area was very negative. Nurses from another service area were very diverse in their responses – perhaps reflecting the diversity of provision and different service models which existed within the Trust as a legacy from the past.

Increasing the involvement of clinicians in decision making

I asked the nurses for the factors that, in their opinion, increased the involvement of clinicians in decision making.

Two factors were rated by all respondents as essential or important:

• Good relationships between managers and clinicians
• A feeling that my contribution makes a difference

'A climate of openness and honesty' was identified by almost everyone (98%) as essential or important.

Five other factors were rated by over 90% as essential or important:

• Mutual respect between all players
• Support for innovative and creative practice
• Clear boundaries within which to operate
• Control over resources at service level
• The existence of formal structures which facilitate involvement – such as the Clinical Management Teams (CMTs)

I also asked the nurse managers to rate the effectiveness, in their opinion, of a number of different avenues for influencing decisions within the Trust. The results are shown in Table 2.

Table 2: Perceptions of the most effective way of influencing decisions within the Trust

Percentage of respondents:	Very effective	Effective	Not sure	Ineffective	Totally ineffective
A As a member of a Clinical Management Team	25	36	33	3	3
B Through my line manager	5	50	26	16	3
C Meetings with the Chief Executive	17	8	58	14	3
D Meetings with senior management	13	58	21	8	
E Through a trade union	5	22	30	43	
F Workshops involving Managers and Clinicians	42	40	18		

The interviewees – the senior managers and chairs of the CMTs – had said that the most effective mechanisms for engaging clinical staff in the decision making process, from their point of view, were:

- Meetings with senior management, particularly the Chief Executive and Director of Patient Services, both formally and informally
- Workshops in which a larger number of stakeholders could be involved
- Membership of Clinical Management Teams – the CMTs were seen by all interviewees as important and potentially effective forums for service-focused decision making, and the key to developing and delivering the Clinical Governance agenda. However, the interviewees said that the role and function of the CMTs should be reviewed and strengthened to enable them to take on a governance role.

The value of these three avenues of influence was on the whole echoed by the nurse managers' responses in Table 2 – with the exception of direct contact with the Chief Executive. The low rating for direct contact with the Chief Executive perhaps reflected the fact that the nurse managers would have far fewer opportunities to use this avenue than the more senior interviewees.

Other popular avenues of influence noted in the survey (in response to an open question) were staff/team meetings (35 responses) and involving staff in a change process/using a participative leadership style (15 responses)

The nurse managers were asked to rate the importance of being involved in certain specific decisions, which were:

- Clinical policy development
- Development of new services
- Review of existing services
- Budget management at service level
- Developing the values and principles of the organisation
- Contract negotiation
- Quality development e.g. standard setting, protocols, CQI projects
- Identifying cost improvement initiatives
- Recruitment of staff
- Determining clinical audit priorities

All respondents indicated that it was very important or important to be involved in four of these areas

- 'Recruitment of staff' was seen by 87% of the nurses as very important and 13% as important.
- 'Development of new services' was rated by 74% as very important and 26% as important
- 'Review of existing services' was identified by 68% as very important and 32% as important
- 'Clinical policy development' was identified by 63% as very important and 37% as important

Review

> 'Involve all personnel at all levels in all functions in virtually everything'
>
> Peters (1988)

Although the Trust had expressed a commitment to partnership working and encouraging staff to share their views, and had established a range of formal and informal mechanisms to facilitate these processes, the survey suggested the results were variable and dependent on the position of individuals in the organisational.

The study indicated that the nurse managers were willing to be more involved in the decision making process, but in some service areas they were quite clearly frustrated with a system which marginalised them from contributing to decisions about the services they deliver.

The Clinical Management Teams were viewed by almost all respondents as important and potentially effective forums for service-focused decision making and the key to delivering the Clinical Governance agenda – although the interviewees identified an urgent need to strengthen the role and function of CMTs, to ensure they were equipped, resourced and empowered to take on a governance role.

The 'whole-systems shared governance model' described by Porter O'Grady et al (1997) would offer a radical and arguably more appropriate system for organisational decision making for healthcare in the 21st century. Clinical Management Teams could form the foundation for a Trust wide shared governance model if reconstituted along these lines.

Workshops were cited by the majority of respondents in both stages of the study as the most effective way of engaging clinical input. Workshops allow a larger number of individuals to contribute to the process and therefore build commitment to the outcome. They also remove individuals from their normal functional role which facilitates a more open and equitable dialogue between participants.

The key characteristics of good practice in collaborative decision making, which emerged from the interviews and were endorsed by the nurse managers, were:

- Good working relationships, based on mutual respect, equity and partnership;
- The sharing of a common value system;
- Development of a shared vision for the service;
- Clarity of responsibility and designated authority;
- Managers who adopt a facilitating and consensual role, and trust people to get on with the job;
- The existence of an honest and open climate;
- Fostering a 'can do' mentality;
- Having protected time, access to information and adequate resources to make an effective contribution;

- Feeling that the individual's contribution makes a difference to organisational performance;
- Feeling personally valued.

The survey emphasises that responsibility for meeting the fundamental challenge of how to engage clinicians more effectively in decision making lies with the leaders of healthcare organisations, who must create an environment which fosters co-operation and collaboration based on a participative approach to management.

Postscript

At the time of writing, I am Director of Nursing and Primary Care Development for Wakefield West Primary Care Trust, which was established on 1 April 2001. In my current role I am responsible for the delivery of Primary Care Trust services, the development and integration of primary care and workforce development, and I also have the strategic Board lead for clinical governance.

A key element of the Government's commitment to modernising the NHS is the involvement of practising clinicians in decision making. The constitution of Primary Care Trusts embraces this concept through the establishment of a professional Executive Committee, which brings together both managers and clinical professionals to manage the Primary Care Trust agenda.

The principles of shared governance are the foundation on which the culture of Wakefield West Primary Care Trust is being developed – actively involving clinicians in Wakefield is 'the way we do things here' with early indications that this is the only way to successfully modernise and deliver the NHS Plan.

Although my research influenced change in my former organisation, I feel privileged to be a founding Director in a new organisation, and to be instrumental in building an organisational culture which totally embraces clinical involvement and the principles of equity, ownership, partnership, and accountability.

Three years on, we are well on the way to the Holy Grail!

References

Buchan, J. (1997) 'Magnet Hospitals' *Nursing Standard;* Vol. 12 No 7.

Department of Health (1997).

The New NHS 'Modern: Dependable' London: HMSO.

Department of Health (1998) *First Class Service* London: HMSO.

Drucker P. (1989) *The New Realities* New York: Harper and Row.

Drucker P. (1995) *The Changing World of the Executive* Oxford: Butterworth.

Evans K., Aubry K., Hawkins M., Curley T. and Porter O'Grady T. (1995) Whole Systems Shared Governance, A Model for the Integrated Health System *JONA* Vol 25, No 5.

Hammer M. and Champy J. (1994) *Reengineering the Corporation* London: Nicholas Brearley Ltd.

Hand M. (1995) 'Empowerment: You Can't Give It, People Have Got To Want It' *Management Development Review* Vol. 8. No 3 pp 36–40.

Manthey M. (1998) *Handbook for Leading an Empowered Organisation* Unpublished.

McLagan P. and Nel C. (1995) *The Age of Participation* San Francisco: Berrett-Koehler.

Oppenheim A.N. (1986) *Questionnaire Design and Attitude Measurement* Aldershot: Gower.

Peters T. (1988) *Thriving on Chaos* London: Guild Publishing.

Porter O'Grady T. (1992) *Implementing Shared Governance* St Louis: Mosby Year Book.

Porter O'Grady T. and Kreuger Wilson C. (1995) *The Leadership Revolution in Health Care* Maryland: Aspen.

Porter O'Grady T., Hawkins M.A. and Parker M.L. (1997) *Whole-Systems Shared Governance* Maryland: Aspen.

Senge P.M. (1992) *The Fifth Discipline* London: Century Business.

- Andrea Hopkins also led the Improving Working Lives Taskforce for the Northern and Yorkshire Region. The aim of the Taskforce was to champion a healthy work-life balance and improve employment practices as part of a strategy to attract, recruit and retain the workforce needed for the delivery of high quality patient care. She continues to work a four-day week, as a personal commitment to achieving a healthy work-life balance.

CHAPTER TEN

Organisational learning and organisational development

Mark Crowther

Introduction

This chapter describes a research project I carried out in 1997 into organisational learning in the context of an Acute NHS Trust.

At that time I had a personal and professional need to learn and understand more about the concept of organisational learning. I also wanted to take time to understand how the Trust where I worked could seriously develop itself to improve its culture, fortify its position in the market place and enhance its reputation as a major provider of healthcare services. The NHS was then undergoing enormous change. In this particular Trust it was a time of significant uncertainty as to the future of the organisation, and to work through this change the Trust needed to learn, and to learn rapidly. The pace of change in the NHS has not slowed in any way in recent times, and I believe that organisational learning is as relevant now as it was at the time I carried out this project.

The Trust was a provider of both general and specialist acute hospital services, employing approximately 2500 whole time equivalent staff, with a contract income of around £65m and serving a local population of 350,000 residents. The nature of service provision, however, dictated that services be provided on a supra-regional, national and international scale.

The timing of this research dovetailed with other Organisation Development work that I was already undertaking in the Trust, and I was able to gauge the capability of the Trust to engage in effective organisational learning by analysing a survey of key aspects of the organisation's culture.

Organisational culture

The two concepts of organisational culture and organisational learning have gained much prominence in management thinking as organisations strive for continued success.

Culture can be seen as one of the keys to the pursuit of organisational excellence. Peters and Waterman (1982) identified a need for a strong culture in their work on excellent companies. To them strength of culture comes from the shared values and norms of behaviour usually associated with strong leadership and focused on the market, on the customer, and on matching the product or service with customer demand.

Schein (1984) and Williams et al (1993) agree that culture is determined by a series of beliefs, attitudes and deeply held values. Culture is thus a powerful aspect of organisational life and yet appears to be largely intangible and invisible. Egan (1994:88) described covert culture as 'the beliefs, values and norms that are not named, at least not publicly, but nevertheless drive patterns of behaviour'.

In the health care setting the way we do things is heavily influenced by a multitude of factors, not least of which are the overt issues of hierarchy and functionality and the more covert aspects of professional tribalism and territorialism. Senge et al for example (1994: 479) talk of 'the special role that professionals play'.

A number of authors have identified different types of culture (eg Edwards and Kleiner, 1988, Pheysey, 1993), however as Egan and Hall suggest (1994: 2) 'There is no such thing as a perfect culture. The one that serves your business is the one you need'. Healthcare organisations undergoing massive structural as well as operational change, need a suitably flexible culture, as described by Weightman (1996) as leaning toward a more entrepreneurial style rather than the older, sluggish bureaucratic environment.

For organisational learning to take place, the organisation's culture needs to place a high value on learning, and learning needs to be promoted and practised.

Organisational learning

In many ways the development of thinking around the subject of organisational culture has mirrored the development of a body of knowledge around the idea of a Learning Organisation and even more recently, and seemingly more achievable, the notion or concept of organisational learning. I say more achievable because the idea of an organisation learning appears more tangible and indeed more possible than the ethereal concept of a whole Learning Organisation. The idea of a Learning Organisation leads to such questions as 'how do we know when we are?' or 'is it a possibility?' and even more worryingly the belief amongst operational managers that they have actually achieved this ideal when in truth their energies are spent on reactive management which fortifies the already unlearning, hierarchically bureaucratic structures of some of today's organisations, particularly within the Acute sector of the NHS.

Perhaps the idea of organisational learning is particularly attractive because it can be applied and illustrated at different levels and parts of an organisation rather than needing to fulfil the whole. Pedler et al (1997) talk of this more pragmatic concept and relate it to the development of organisational processes, learning to benefit the company. This immediately sounds far more attainable, indeed possible, than becoming a Learning Organisation. Yet compare this to Senge et al (1994: 479) who quite clearly support the notion of the Learning Organisation and with specific reference to the provision of healthcare when they argue that, 'Hospitals can become true learning organisations, in every sense of the word'.

The concept of organisational learning is a progression of the idea of a Learning Organisation. Pearn et al (1995) encapsulate this when they say:

> We are not sure if there is such a thing as *the* Learning Organisation in the sense that the possession of a number of characteristics means that an organisation is entitled to be called the Learning Organisation. We are sure, however, that some organisations are better at learning than others.

This immediately questions *the* Learning Organisation and introduces a further element to the debate, that of a range of characteristics which enable some organisations to learn better than others.

One of the key characteristics of a learning organisation will, quite simply, be a culture and a climate that encourage learning. As Pedler et al (1997) explain, this climate should be exemplified by the behaviour of managers demonstrating that their ultimate priority is to facilitate the learning of others – not to exert control over them. This leads to the question, 'what happens when a mistake is made?' Hopefully it will be viewed as a learning opportunity and not an opportunity to seek to blame. As Pedler et al (1997:180) note: 'How mistakes are handled is an instructive marker of the overall climate of the company'.

Senge (1990) argues that, 'The organisations that will truly excel in the future will be the organisations that discover how to tap people's commitment and capacity to learn at *all* levels in the organisation'.

In nurturing the environment conducive to the learning of all its members the company must find a way of harnessing all the expended energy and using it for its own transformation. Without this harnessing process the potential for organisational learning to take place is reduced and the opportunity for transformation, potentially lost.

If a positive culture is one essential characteristic of a learning organisation, other key features appear to be:

- visionary leadership
- teamworking and team learning
- a range of supportive structures and processes

Mayo & Lank (1994) regard leadership as being about visioning, risk taking, empowering, learning, coaching and collaborating, which influence organisational culture and have an impact on the very way that people act and interrelate.

Senge et al (1994) clearly state that the development of a learning culture must begin with the top of the organisation and what they describe as 'the critical role of leadership'. This role is further explained in powerful terms as being to:

> launch a full scale dedicated effort to change the entire culture of the hospital, including the relationships among all its functions and operations. (p. 480)

Stimulating, dynamic visionary leadership therefore feels to be a cornerstone in the pursuit of organisational learning and this translates into the ways in which the leader/s establish norms, patterns of behaviour and organisational structures, systems and processes to enable and empower the organisation to perform (Pearn et al 1995, Moss-Jones 1994).

A feature of much of the work on the concept of organisational learning has been the belief that teamworking or team learning plays a large part in determining the success or otherwise of the organisation (Senge 1990, Pedler et al 1997, Pedler and Aspinwall 1996, Pearn et al 1995). This goes hand in hand with the idea of empowerment, and the belief that self-managing teams can be empowered to attain higher levels of performance.

Team *working* suggests a group of people working well together to achieve a desired output or service but I believe team *learning* to be more than that. It is the culmination of effective team working done with synergistic ease. It is about the 'We' not the 'I' and the ability to develop a shared team vision and to *really* listen to each other and to understand.

Yet the paradox remains that many of our organisations are not ready to create and sustain this approach, many parts of the NHS are still relying heavily on controlling hierarchies because that is their history and what they know and understand regardless of its effectiveness.

Structures can support or can hinder organisational learning. A Learning Organisation must develop that structure which both allows for team learning, empowerment, sharing and all the other key aspects already discussed and is right for its own situation – its product, service, market etc.

Too often we see organisations impose a structure on themselves which does not readily suit their operating style or purpose. The NHS has amongst its Trusts a variety of types of structure some more appropriate and suitable than others. Rigid hierarchies stifle innovation and creativity and thus learning.

The survey

The organisational culture survey was carried out with the full and explicit support of the Trust Board and Senior Management Team, at a time of significant change and uncertainty for the organisation.

Very significantly there was a poor response, only 191 (or 13%) of those surveyed returning their forms complete, thus making the findings statistically invalid.

This was disappointing, as the forms were distributed to a truly representative cross section of the population of the Trust, both vertically and horizontally. I feel the low response reflected the nervous reluctance of people to offer views and opinions about an organisation in crisis.

The survey focused on the culture of the organisation and those cultural issues that were deemed sufficiently important to impact on the effective working of the Trust.

There is not space here to dwell upon the details of the responses, so I will focus on the main patterns of response in the relation to the four key characteristics, identified in the previous section, that support organisational learning:

- leadership
- the development of a learning culture or climate
- the existence of enabling as opposed to disabling structures
- the need to foster a team working and team learning approach to running organisations

The overriding message concerning leadership was significantly quite negative. One of the key attributes of an effective leader is to listen, but 57% of respondents disagreed with the statement 'I feel I have the opportunity to have my voice heard', and 24% neither agreed nor disagreed. The following comments were offered to support the view expressed.

'The lower you are the less you're listened to.'
'Who listens? Senior Managers certainly don't.'

There was a very clear view that people did not feel valued or recognised by the Trust Board or Senior Management Team of the organisation but felt quite strongly valued by their colleagues and line managers. Allowing for a certain element of senior management detachment which will inevitably account for some of the opinion, 72% and 56% respectively felt undervalued by the Trust Board and Senior Management Team and 62% and 83% respectively felt valued by their line manager and colleagues. This said much about the solidarity of teams and the potentially disabling structures that form barriers between operational teams and the management hierarchy. Localised or team leadership seemed to work well but organisational leadership was severely criticised.

Favourable responses to questions about the ability to be open and honest, the confidence to challenge work practices and the support offered by the local environment/ departments again said a lot about the climate created within teams and departments and the atmosphere engendered by line management. A picture emerged of an organisation split in half horizontally, with a reasonably productive and engaging culture at the operational level constantly fighting and struggling with the upper echelons who are perhaps detached and remote, yet have such a major impact on the way they establish the tone and organisational norms.

There were some empowering and some disempowering structural factors. 61% of respondents felt that the Trust's communication processes did not make them feel a part of the organisation, and a significant percentage felt that senior management largely failed to satisfy the needs of the organisation in communicating timely and appropriate information. However, there was a supportive climate at a department/unit level. At the operational sharp end, it appeared that enabling and empowering structures existed and worked with a degree of effectiveness.

The emphasis on teams within the Trust was a recurrent theme and certainly the evidence in the survey suggested that people gained a lot from their immediate work teams. Unfortunately this team philosophy did not appear to exist up the hierarchy, in the perception of the respondents, particularly at a senior management level. There was little evidence to suggest that the Trust valued a team approach or rewarded teamworking – thus the ability to learn as a team was greatly reduced.

The responses to the survey made quite disappointing reading and yet contained more than a glimmer of hope. It was evident that the respondents cared about their jobs, their roles, their colleagues and their working environments. The basic ingredients for developing the organisation existed in abundance.

The survey suggested that there were many people within the organisation sufficiently committed, and with sufficient energy, to drive or initiate change. As Lichfold notes (1997:38)

> A successful learning organisation relies heavily on change agents to manage, drive and support the process. There are three principal types of change agent: the champion – who provides leadership; the implementor – who makes it happen; and the facilitator – who provides guidance and support along the way.

Developing people to act as change agents was one possible strategy. The organisation could draw on the commitment and energy of its staff to develop its champions, its implementors and its facilitators.

A key area for development was the leadership of the Trust. Leadership that is respected and valued is essential for organisational learning. Leadership must, over time change the climate of the organisation to one that listens, learns, enables and empowers.

As Alimo-Metcalfe (1996) says:

> Organisations with senior managers who are perceived as transformational leaders characterised as visionary, enthusiastic, encouraging constructive criticism and showing concern for others, are significantly more effective than those managed by those who control performance mainly through the application of structures, rules, rewards and punishments.

Personal learning

Returning to my rationale for undertaking this work I identified a personal development need to learn more about organisational learning and in terms of my future to use this learning in my organisational development work.

What then did I learn?

- To be effective in Organisation Development, you need to really understand the organisation and how it works before you suggest a course of action for change.
- Leadership is of absolute importance and influence in organisations.
- Organisational culture can be very strong, and it is very difficult to actually change culture without identifying the key levers – leadership, teamworking and supportive structures and processes.
- It is crucially important to involve people and to build participation when engaging in the change process.
- Be pragmatic and realistic: realise that organisational development takes time. Early wins work wonders, and people need to see meaningful action. Only then will lasting change result.
- Value what works. Build on what is good.

- Above all, be flexible in your response. No one strategy or approach can always be appropriate and so a range of interventions will be needed to ensure success.

Postscript

Reflecting on this analysis has proved to be a very useful process in terms of my own learning and how I continue to facilitate organisational development interventions. It is clear to me that leadership is a crucial ingredient in determining or influencing organisational culture and, allied to positive structures and teams within organisations, can lead to progress. The individual competencies of those charged with taking the lead, however, must be geared to the characteristics and strategies identified in this work, otherwise the organisation can appear divided and lacking direction as well as creating great frustration in those attempting to carry out the real work at the operational end of the organisation.

References

Alimo-Metcalfe, B. (1996) The Feedback Revolution. *Health Service Journal.* 13/06/96. pp. 26–28.

Edwards, J. D., & Kleiner, B.H. (1988) Transforming Values and Culture Effectively. *Leadership and Organisation Development Journal.* 9/1. pp. 13–16.

Egan, G., & Hall, D. (1994) Cultivate Your Culture. *Management Today.* April 94.

Egan, G. (1994) *Working The Shadowside.* San Francisco: Jossey Bass.

Lichfold, G. (1997) News Scan. *Organisations and People.* AMED. 4:1. pp. 10–14.

Mayo, A., & Lank, E. (1994) The Power Of Learning. *Lecture given at IPD Conference Harrogate.*

Moss-Jones, J. (1994) *Learning Organisation Concepts, Practices and Relevance.* Bristol. NHSTD.

Pearn, M., Roderick, C., & Mulrooney, C. (1995) *Learning Organisations in Practice.* Maidenhead. McGraw Hill.

Pedler, M., & Aspinwall, K. (1996) *'Perfect PLC?'* Maidenhead. McGraw Hill.

Pedler, M., Burgoyne,J., & Boydell, T. (1997) *The Learning Company A Strategy for Sustainable Development.* Maidenhead: McGraw Hill.

Peters, T.J., & Waterman, R.H. (1982) *In Search of Excellence.* London: Harper and Row.

Pheysey, D. C. (1993) *Organisational Cultures Types and Transformations.* London. Routledge.

Schein, E.H. (1984) Coming To A New Awareness Of Organisational Culture. *Sloan Management Review.* Winter 84. Mass. Institute of Technology.

Senge, P. (1990) *The Fifth Discipline.* London: Century.

Senge, P., Roberts,C., Ross, R.B., Smith, B.J., & Kleiner, A. (1994) *The Fifth Discipline Fieldbook.* London. Brealey.

Weightman, J. (1996) *Managing People in The Health Service.* London. IPD.

Williams, A., Dobson, P., & Walton, M. (1993) *Changing Culture – New Organisational Approaches* (2nd Edition). London: IPM.

■ Mark Crowther is currently a self employed OD Consultant working across business sectors, retaining a special interest in healthcare having worked in the NHS for 14 years. He can be contacted at markcrowther@lineone.net

CHAPTER ELEVEN

Values and culture in an NHS Trust

Mary Courtney

Introduction

This study investigates the values of Trust Board directors, managers and doctors within a large community and mental health services NHS trust, serving a city that has a population of three-quarters of a million. The organisation is large, disparate, and at the time of this research, the services provided had been under one management for only 4 years. The study suggests that the value systems of doctors within an NHS Trust differ from those of directors and managers in certain specific areas. There is some evidence of three separate subcultures within the Trust and this has implications for leadership and management.

Organisational culture

Culture as a concept developed in the first half of the 20th century through the work of anthropologists and sociologists. Kroeber and Kluckhohn (1952) provide 164 definitions of culture, and conclude:

> '... we think culture is a product; is historical; includes ideas, patterns and values; is selective; is learned; is based upon symbols; and is an abstraction from behaviour and the products of behaviour'
>
> page 157

This anthropological view of culture has been transposed onto organisational cultures in ways that may be inappropriate. Thus, while using the word 'culture' popular texts such as Deal and Kennedy (1982) and Peters and Waterman (1982) treat organisational culture as if it is an independent variable which is created by leaders and can be manipulated and changed. Smircich (1983), Meek (1988) and Meyerson and Martin (1987), however, all take the anthropological view that culture in organisations is what the organisation *is* rather than something the organisation *has*. Thus they view culture as a root metaphor and as socially emergent, rather than belonging to the management. This view of culture is enlarged by Morgan (1986) in his description of culture as a metaphor for organisations.

Organisational culture has become a dominant topic in organisational thinking over the last 15 years, predominantly because of the postulated association between organisational culture and performance. Peters and Waterman (1982, page 75) state:

> 'Without exception, the dominance and coherence of culture proved
> to be an essential quality of the excellent companies.'.

A variety of definitions of culture are available, the populist version of Bower (quoted in Deal and Kennedy 1982) is *'the way we do things around here'*, while Williams et al (1993 page 14) expand on this behavioural definition to include cognitive aspects:

> 'Culture is the commonly held and relatively stable beliefs, attitudes
> and values that exist within the organisation.'

Sathe (1985) gives a more extensive description of culture including organisational behaviour patterns, justifications of behaviour, and underlying basic assumptions, meaning those beliefs and values that are internalised and thus belong to the individual but are shared with the community.

Schein (1992), in common with Williams et al (1993) emphasises the existence of different levels of culture. The most superficial level of culture is most clearly visible, for example architecture, modes of dress, patterns of behaviour. At a deeper level are the 'espoused values', those values and beliefs written in company documents and spoken about by management, which may not represent reality. The deepest level of culture on which the true culture is based consists of what Schein calls 'basic underlying assumptions', those taken-for-granted, shared beliefs which underly the ways of working of the organisation. Schein writes (1992, p26):

'the essence of a culture lies in the pattern of basic underlying assumptions, and once one understands those, one can easily understand the other more surface levels and deal more appropriately with them'.

These basic underlying assumptions are called 'values' by the majority of other authors.

Anthropologists Kroeber and Kluckhohn (1952) emphasise the pivotal position of values in cultures, stating:

'... values provide the only basis for any intelligible comprehension of culture...'

page 173

A similar position has been taken by a number of organisational theorists, who describe values as:

'beliefs and moral principles that lie behind a company's culture'

Campbell and Yeung 1994

'principles or standards of an individual, group, organisation'

Kenny 1994

'preferences about desired organisational outcomes'

Hage and Dewar 1973

'broad, non-specific feelings .... that are often unconscious and rarely discussable, that cannot be observed as such but are manifested in alternatives of behaviour'

Hofstede et al 1990

Kabanoff and Holt (1996) point out that values may be studied as single entities but in practice form systems. Similarly, Smircich (1983) discusses 'systems of knowledge and beliefs', Hofstede et al (1990) describe 'dimensions of value systems' in his study of cross-national cultures, and in Deal and Kennedy (1982) a 'shared system of values' is stated to be a feature of strong culture companies. Other investigators of culture have developed typologies of systems which characterise behaviour in different companies. The most popular of these is Harrison (1972) who describes four types of ideological style: power, role, task and person. Underlying these four styles are systems of thought which parallel Schein's basic assumptions. This way of understanding organisational culture has been enlarged and popularised by Handy (1991).

In reality it is likely that values exist both as single entities and systems and that the mode of enquiry will determine to some extent what is uncovered.

Cultures and subcultures

Some authors on the topic of culture (for example, Peters and Waterman 1982, Deal and Kennedy 1982) give the impression that corporate culture should be a uniform entity, that organisations are like holograms, and that cultural differences are deviant. The positive impact of culture on performance is related to 'strong' and homogeneous cultures.

There is evidence, however, of the existence of subcultures in many organisations. Martin and Siehl (1983) write that:

> 'organisational cultures are composed of various interlocking, nested, sometimes conflicting subcultures'

> page 53

These subcultures may enhance one another, or conflict with one another, or be largely congruent with one another.

Within the NHS, Pettigrew et al (1992) state:

> 'it is not possible …… to talk of a single culture, but rather of a collection of different subcultures that may inhabit the same district'

> page 281

Weisbord (1976) identifies three social systems within American medical centres, while Kouzes and Mico (1979) describe three 'domains' within human service organisations – policy, management and service.

Mark and Scott (1992) have related domain theory to the NHS, stating:

> 'what is common to all parts of the NHS, whether it is one organisation or a series, is the existence of its three domains'

> page 215

These domains are:

- political
- managerial, and
- professional

The research project

I set out to investigate the values of representatives of the three domains of an NHS trust, through unstructured interviews and subsequent analysis of the interview content. I interviewed two representatives of each domain – two board members, two managers and two consultants. The selection of subjects was purposive, not random, as it was important to choose subjects who were likely to be honest, communicative and reflective.

In choosing people to interview, I considered the spectrum of experience they represented, for while wishing to have interviewees representing diversity of experience it was also important to have conformity within the domain they represented. Thus, for example, for conformity, the political domain was represented by two board members who did not have health professional backgrounds, but in order to also encourage diversity a specific choice was made to interview one executive and one non-executive director. Similarly, the professionals were both consultant psychiatrists, but worked in different specialties and locations. The managers were both senior and from management backgrounds but while one worked within headquarters the other was an operational manager.

The interviews were aimed at eliciting the subject's values in relation to their work but had no other formal agenda. The content of the interview followed the subjects' cues. Each interview lasted between 40 and 55 minutes, and was terminated when it appeared appropriate on either side.

Each interview was tape-recorded and transcribed, and the transcripts were divided into *meaning units* which were then sorted and categorised. Burnard (1994) defines a meaning unit as:

> 'a discrete phrase, sentence or series of sentences which conveys one idea or one related set of perceptions'.

Sorting and categorisation of meaning units was conducted manually. As recommended by Glaser and Strauss (1967) single meaning units were sorted into more than one category, where this was appropriate.

Division of the interview scripts into meaning units gave a total of 1271 meaning units. Sorting the meaning units gave rise to 6 main categories, each with subcategories.

Summary of findings

The study provided some confirmation of the existence of three domains within the NHS, although the results must be treated with caution because of the small and limited sample.

The values common to all three groups were equity and providing health care services. While doctors valued team working, board members and managers were concerned with effectiveness, efficiency, valuing staff, relationships with the public, the purchasers and the providers, and looking ahead.

The board members and managers had similar values which broadly speaking reiterated the values of the NHS and locally relate to the provision of effective, efficient services to the population, and valuing staff within the organisation. The values of board members and managers were congruent, but each reflected a different sphere of attention: board members were preoccupied by the environment and future strategies, while managers concentrated on operational issues. Both were concerned about finance and the need for efficiency and effectiveness. The congruence between their value systems may reflect the seniority of the two managers.

The consultant interviews were dominated by consideration of their values in relation to the service they provide to individual patients, and contained little reference to the organisation. It appeared that the doctors' value of service to the individual patient, whatever the cost, was in conflict with the values of boards and managers, who had a wider view and emphasised efficient resource use. Doctors also placed a high value on working within teams.

Areas of dissonance between doctors and the other two groups were likely to relate to resource constraints and the need for prioritisation (see for example Mascie-Taylor 1983, Wall 1997).

Similarities and contrasts between the groups are illustrated in specific examples from the interviews. The main categories to emerge from the sorting of the interview transcripts were:

- direct values
- the environment
- staff
- relationships
- service and
- finance.

We will briefly consider each of them in turn

Direct values

This category represented statements of general principle, some of which were enlarged and clarified in further categories. Table 1 shows how the meaning units have sorted numerically into selected subcategories. The actual numbers of meaning units within each subcategory do not necessarily bear a direct relationship with the importance of that topic to the interviewee, but they may indicate the spread of interest in the categories between the interviewees.

The first subcategory – General Statements – contains some general statements by subjects demonstrating their understanding of the term 'values' and its application. While a board member and manager clearly indicated their understanding of values as contributing to the purpose of

Table 1: Numbers of meaning units by subject and subcategory category 1 direct values

	B1	B2	C1	C2	M1	M2	Total
1a General statements	6	2	10	12	15	3	48
1b Personal values	4	–	25	29	14	6	78
1c Humanity	1	2	10	–	1	1	15
1d Organisational	18	16	3	1	33	21	92
1e The NHS	9	13	1	–	1	10	34

B1, B2 = Board members, C1, C2 = Consultants, M1, M2 = Managers the organisation, the consultants saw values as pertaining mainly to their work, and one consultant stated:

'I don't think the organisation has any values'.

Personal values (sub-category 1b) are those statements clearly made by individuals to reflect a personal belief held strongly, though the belief may relate to their own life or their work. The consultants made many such statements compared to board members and managers, and the overriding theme in consultants values is their care of the patients, as exemplified by one doctor's initial comment:

'Number 1 – patients first'.

Other more general personal and humanitarian values are equity, fairness and a belief in people.

Values concerning the organisation and the NHS (1d and 1e) featured frequently in the interviews of board members and managers. Board members and managers alike expressed a belief in the core principles of the NHS, particularly that it should be free at the point of delivery, and equitable. Organisational values of the board members concerned delivery of good service equitably, developing services, valuing staff and protecting them from political pressures. Managers emphasised the provision of good quality services within the resources available, and the way the organisation valued staff and treated them well.

The environment

This category contained statements relating to the environment of the Trust – covering issues of national politics, relationships with other local trusts, and other local relationships – including relating to the public. As may be expected the board members were particularly concerned with this aspect of their work. Over 80% of the meaning units in this category came from board members. One consultant made no reference at all to aspects of organisational environment.

The board members were concerned about the influence of political pressures regarding finance and provision of service, which they had to balance with their beliefs about local services and the Trust.

Staff

Board members and managers both discussed staff – but consultants made no comments in this area.

Board members described rewarding staff through pay rises. Both board members took pride in having quickly settled the latest pay award at the maximum and hence being criticised by other local trust boards. The board members saw themselves as 'good employers'.

While the board members made statements about valuing staff, the managers were not so sure this happened in practice:

> '(staff) may feel that the trust makes some nice rosy statements about valuing people, quite a few of them, I think, don't feel that that is the case'.

The board members saw their contact with staff on an informal basis as very important. They valued staff presentations to the board and the opportunity to visit groups of staff within the trust as opportunities for exchange of ideas. Similarly, one manager valued 'getting out and about in amongst the services' as a way of keeping in touch. Communication was more of an issue for the managers; board members valued bottom-up communication – finding out what was going on from staff – and seemed not to be concerned about top-down communication. Managers were more concerned that top-down communication should be improved.

Relationships

This large category concerned all relationships, and contained the sub-categories of team working and interprofessional relationships that were of great concern to the consultants. Some of the smaller categories could have been combined, but conceptually appeared to stand alone. The non-executive board member made no contribution in this category, possibly reflecting his lack of involvement in operational matters.

Table 2: Numbers of meaning units by subject and subcategory category 4 relationships

	B1	B2	C1	C2	M1	M2	Total
4a Team working	–	–	25	99	–	–	124
4b Interprofessional	–	–	1	33	–	–	34
4c Managers on doctors	3	–	–	–	2	38	43
4d Doctors on managers	–	–	5	–	–	–	5
4e Managers	1	–	–	–	4	4	9
4f Relationships in general	3	–	5	5	3	6	22
4g Power and influence	–	–	34	24	–	25	83
4h Tensions and conflict	11	–	7	2	16	7	43
4i Battle and compromise	4	–	8	1	24	1	38

B1, B2 = Board members, C1, C2 = Consultants, M1, M2 = Managers

Team working was valued by the consultants who both believed they should be the leader of 'their' multidisciplinary team. Board members and managers failed to mention team working. One consultant discussed the issue of his own leadership in different team settings, while the other described at length his values within multidisciplinary team working. Issues around team working were also allied with interprofessional relationships.

Service

Within this category were values pertaining to aspects of service delivery.

The board members emphasised their wish to provide good quality services, protected from political pressure. Board members and managers mentioned future service development. Consultants reiterated their values around the medical care of their patients, and their view of themselves as being in a position to judge patients needs and make decisions about who gets what, how and where. Consultants were aware of constraints in their ability to provide their ideal, for instance:

> 'I could provide a much better service, I think it's a disgrace that patients get on average 6 minutes with me 4 times a year, that is appalling'

'I ... try and actually provide the service that the patient seems to need within the constraints of the service'.

A manager expressed similar sentiments:

'you get those kind of real dilemmas where you know the service you're providing is at such a low level'.

Board members did not refer to service constraints.

Both board members and managers were concerned about the effectiveness of services, believing that the services of the Trust should be evidence-based and that research should be encouraged.

Finance

The board members wished to ensure that the Trust had enough income and were very concerned that the money they had was used wisely, a view echoed by one of the managers. One consultant believed that cost should not be considered when treating individuals, but that having some budgetary control might enable him to make better decisions about service provision.

Different cultures

The differences between the values held by the consultants and those held by the board members and managers were particularly interesting, as both consultants were positively chosen to take part in the project in the knowledge that they were respected by their colleagues and the management, and that both currently chaired committees within the trust. I deliberately chose not to interview consultants who were expected to hold very strong medicalist beliefs.

However, Kouzes and Mico's domain theory (1979) predicted that the values of professionals would differ from those of the other two domains. They state that the professional domain operates by the principles of autonomy and self-regulation and that professionals work in *'individualised, client-specific problem solving'* modes.

The values of doctors are reinforced by continuing education and socialisation and are likely to be well established. The 'core values' for the medical profession produced by a joint medical conference in 1994 emphasise service to the individual patient as the prime value (Core Values 1994). The values include doctors' role in advising on priorities for health care and offering service to communities but there is no mention of responsibility to the organisation within which the health care is delivered. Differences in medical/managerial values have been observed before (for example Litwinenko and Cooper 1994, Preston et al 1996). Harrison et al (1992) state:

> 'doctors ... subscribe to, and are motivated by, different sets of values and objectives from those of managers'

> page 101

Pettigrew et al (1992) note:

> 'the tension between medical and managerial constituencies is part of the whole architecture of the NHS'.

> page 151

In this project, relationships between doctors and management were highlighted by some interviewees (in the category Relationships). One board member believed there was a 'healthy tension', but one manager expressed concern about the power of consultants within the trust:

> 'with the power of being consultant is the responsibility as well around how they perform their own personal part of the job but how they again facilitate other people in doing their contributions as well. – I think sometimes there's not enough thought about the impact of the things that they do on other professions, other services, financial resources –'

One consultant made critical comments about managers, and clearly stated values around his leadership and position within the Trust in the category of power and influence:

> 'I believe that doctors should be the boss, and are qualified to be the boss',

> 'XX [name of manager] is there to provide me with the tools that enable me to do my job. I serve the patients, XX serves me, not the other way round. – every manager is here to serve me to serve the patients.'.

Leading across cultures

The existence of different domains has an implication for successful leadership of the NHS.

Mark and Scott (1992) state:

> 'The future success of the NHS in the UK is … dependent on a shared knowledge and understanding of both the purpose and objectives of the political, managerial and professional domains'.

They advise that the different domains should be identified, their responses interpreted and communication encouraged. Schein (1996b) also emphasises the importance of cross-cultural communication to facilitate alignment of subcultures, and Wall (1997) states:

> 'at the personal level there needs to be more discussion of people's values'.

Kouzes and Mico (1979) offer several suggestions as remedies, including the employment of integrators or establishment of temporary collateral organisations. Mark and Scott (1992)

In practice, genuine dialogue between the domains should be encouraged, and particularly discussion of their value systems. Areas of conflict should be explored and the organisation should work towards producing a statement of values that is agreed by all and that encompasses a mediation of the dilemmas.

This is not to press for a unified culture. Mark and Scott (1992) remind us that:

> 'creative tension … should exist between the three domains … and move the organisation into a creative and dynamic future'.

Thus we are advised to understand and share our understandings, but to be prepared to live with and make use of the tension that is a necessary part of organisations.

References

Burnard, P. (1994) 'Searching for Meaning: a Method of Analysing Interview Transcripts with a Personal Computer' *Nurse Education Today* 14, 111–117.

Campbell, A., Yeung, S. (1994) 'Creating a Sense of Mission' In De Wit, B., Meyer, R., *Strategy: Process, Content, Context* West Publishing.

Core Values for the Medical Profession in the 21st Century *Conference Report* November 1994.

Deal, T., Kennedy, A. (1982) *Corporate Cultures* Penguin Business.

Glaser, B.G., Strauss, A.L. (1967) *The Discovery of Grounded Theory* Aldine de Gruyter New York.

Hage, J., Dewar, R. (1973) 'Elite Values Versus Organizational Structure in Predicting Innovation' *Administrative Science Quarterly* 18 279–290.

Hammersley, M., Atkinson, P. (1995) *Ethnography Principles in Practice* Routledge.

Handy, C. (1991) *Gods of Management* Century Business.

Harrison, R. (1972) 'Understanding Your Organization's Character' *Harvard Business Review* May–June, 119–128

Harrison, S., Hunter, D.J., Marnoch, G., Pollitt, C. (1992) *Just Managing: Power and Culture in the National Health Service* Macmillan.

Hofstede, G., Neuijen, B., Ohayv, D.D., Sanders, G. (1990) 'Meauring Organizational Cultures: A Qualitative and Quantitative Study across Twenty Cases' *Administrative Science Quarterly* 35, 286–316.

Kabanoff, B., Holt, J. (1996) 'Changes in the Espoused Values of Australian Organizations 1986–1990 *Journal of Organizational Behaviour* 17, 201–219.

Kenny, T. (1994) 'From Vision to Reality through Values' *Management Development Review* 7, 3, 17–20.

Kouzes, J., Mico, P.R. (1979) 'Domain Theory: An Introduction to Organizational Behaviour in Human Service Organisations'. *The Journal of Applied Behavioural Science* 449–469.

Kroeber, A.L., Kluckhohn, C. (1952) *Culture: A Critical View of Concepts and Definitions* Vintage Books.

Litwinenko, A., Cooper, C.L. (1994) The Impact of Trust Status on Corporate Culture *Journal of Management in Medicine* 8, 4, 8–17.

Mark, A., Scott, H. (1992) Management in the National Health Service. In: Willcocks, L., Harrow, J. (Eds) *Rediscovering Public Services Management* McGraw-Hill, London.

Martin, J., Siehl, C. (1983) 'Organizational Culture and Counterculture: An Uneasy Symbiosis' *Organizational Dynamics* Autumn 1983 52–64.

Mascie-Taylor, H., Pedler, J., Winkless, A.J. (1983) *Doctors and Dilemmas* Selwood Wentworth Associates.

Meek, V.L. (1988) Organizational Culture: Origins and Weaknesses *Organization Studies* 9/4, 453–473.

Meyerson, D., Martin, J. (1987) Cultural Change: An Integration of Three Different Views *Journal of Management Studies* 24:6, 623–647.

Morgan, G. (1986) *Images of Organizations* Sage.

Peters, T.J., Waterman, R.H. (1982) *In Search of Excellence* Harper Collins.

Pettigrew, A., Ferlie, E., McKee, L. (1992) *Shaping Strategic Change* Sage.

Preston, D., Smith, A., Buchanan, D., Jordan, S. (1996) Symbols of the NHS *Management Learning* 27, 3, 343–357.

Sathe, V. (1985) How to Decipher and Change Corporate Culture. In Kilman, R.H., Saxton, M.J., Serpa, R. (Eds) *Gaining Control of the Corporate Culture* Jossey-Bass.

Schein, E.H. (1990) 'Organizational Culture' *American Psychologist* 45, 2, 109–119.

Schein, E.H. (1992) *Organizational Culture and Leadership* Jossey Bass.

Schein, E.H. (1996) 'Culture: the Missing Concept in Organization Studies' *Administrative Science Quarterly* 41 229–240.

Smircich, L. (1983) Concepts of Culture and Organization Analysis *Administrative Science Quarterly* 28, 339–358.

Wall, A. (1997) 'Motive Power' *Health Service Journal* 24 April 26–27.

Weisbord, M.R. (1976) 'Why Organization Development Hasn't Worked (so far) in Medical Centers' *Health Care Management Review* 1, Spring, 17–28.

Williams, A., Dobson, P., Walters, M. (1993) *Changing Culture* Institute of Personnel Management.

■ Dr Mary Courtney graduated in Medicine in 1975, and proceeded to train in Psychiatry. She has been a Consultant in General Adult Psychiatry since 1985 and throughout her career has been concerned with the development of high quality local services. Since carrying out the research she describes in this chapter, she has moved to the Barnsley Community and Priority Services Trust, where she works as a Consultant Psychiatrist. She is heavily involved in the Clinical Governance agenda.

CHAPTER TWELVE

How do doctors and managers make decisions together?

Tony Dearden

Introduction

The history of the NHS has been described as a power struggle between the two dominant cultural groups, doctors and managers (Harrison et al, 1992). Managers struggle with the fact that doctors enjoy considerable discretion over their work, whereas doctors perceive, with some justification, that the agenda of senior management is that of the government of the day. However, few people would argue that the management-medicine interface is absolutely critical to the performance of the NHS, with the doctor–manager relationship one of both mutual dependence and potential conflict.

In 1998 I carried out a short research project into how these two cultural groups work together to make joint decisions.

Investigating doctor–manager decisions

First, I issued a questionnaire to twelve consultant psychiatrists and twelve managers (Area Managers and Executive Directors); twenty questionnaires were returned, an overall response rate of 83%: nine doctors (75%) and eleven managers (92%) replied. Secondly, I carried out semi-structured interviews with two managers and two consultants about how decisions had been taken in a particular case.

In section one of the questionnaire, respondents were asked to give their opinion about how a series of decisions had been made. Section two asked about the same decisions and asked respondents to state their preference for how those decisions *should* have been made. These sections of the questionnaire were answerable on a four point scale: this was chosen so as to exclude a middle position, as I judged that the middle point – equating to an equal partnership between doctors and managers – might be over utilised as the 'politically correct' response or espoused value.

Sections three and four asked open questions, requiring respondents to reflect back on decisions they had made, and asked for a description of a 'good' decision and a 'bad' decision. A good decision was defined as one in which both the doctor(s) and manager(s) were satisfied with the position reached. From my experience in the NHS I judged such mutual satisfaction to equate to a successful outcome, as both parties would be needed for the decision to be successfully implemented. The questionnaire finished with some questions about triggers that prompted the decisions, the procedure adopted, the time available and seeking general comments and opinion about decision making and the doctor–manager relationship.

The semi-structured interview was not designed until the analysis of the questionnaire responses was completed. I selected the shared doctor–manager decision for closer investigation that was mentioned most frequently in the questionnaire responses. I used a standard interview pro forma, based on a critical incident framework, taking each interviewee through the chosen decision in a chronological manner. The questions were used to elicit detailed descriptions about the actions and behaviour of participants from the beginning to the end of the decision-making process. Each interview lasted 45 minutes and was tape recorded and transcribed.

The qualitative data were analysed using grounded theory (Glaser and Strauss, 1967). Each questionnaire was numbered and the code known only to the clerical worker who administered this part of the project. The code was not translated until the qualitative analysis was completed; only then was it possible to distinguish responses from doctors and managers. The quantitative data from the questionnaires were all tabulated and given a numerical value in order to assist analysis. Finally, the transcribed text from the interviews was examined and used to confirm or refute the categories from the questionnaires and identify any new themes.

The small size of the sample must inevitably lead to some caution in considering the findings of the study and their generalisability, but strong common themes emerged, and this does enhance the credibility of the evidence.

Findings

The results from section one of the questionnaire on 'how decisions have been made' are summarised in Table 1. All decisions except one were either made by managers with relatively little influence from doctors, or by doctors with relatively little influence from managers. There was a

Table 1: Who has most influence on decisions

	Decisions made by:			
	Doctors with minimal influence from managers	Doctors with significant influence from managers	Managers with minimal influence from doctors	Managers with minimal influence from doctors
1. Strategic direction/objectives (mental health)	1	1	8*	1
	[ ]	[1]	[4]*=	[4]*=
2. Resectorisation of general psychiatry	2	5*	4	
	[1]	[5]*	[1]	[2]
3. Service contracts/agreements				11*
	[ ]	[ ]	[4]	[5]*
4. Service development priorities			11*	
	[ ]	[ ]	[6]*	[3]
5. Consultant appointments (who is appointed)	10*	1		
	[5]*	[4]	[ ]	[ ]
6. Reprovision/PFI			10*	1
	[ ]	[ ]	[5]*	[4]
7. Prescribing policy & practice	9*	2		
	[4]*=	[4]*=	[1]	[ ]
8. Cost improvement programme				11*
	[ ]	[ ]	[ ]	[9]*
9. Awarding consultant discretionary points & merit awards	8*	2	1	
	[3]	[6]*	[ ]	[ ]
10. Ward closure – service changes		1	9*	1
	[ ]	[ ]	[4]	[5]*

Number of respondents who ticked each box.
Top line = Managers. Bottom line (in [ ]) = Doctors. Modal response = *

broad agreement between doctors and managers as to who actually took the decisions. The results converted to numerical form are shown in Table 2. This shows that for eight of the ten decisions doctors thought that managers had more power than managers themselves reported.

The results from section two on preferences for 'how decisions should be made' are also summarised in Table 2. There was general agreement as to who should make decisions, but a greater diversity of opinion than in Table 1. For all ten decisions, doctors always wanted more power than managers preferred.

The dissonance, or difference between the real position and the preferred, also shows some interesting and consistent differences between doctors and managers. Firstly, the magnitude of the difference is generally larger for doctors than managers (Table 2). That is the dissonance or, by inference, the degree of dissatisfaction is greater amongst doctors. This dissonance could be reduced by changing doctors' expectations to be more compatible with the 'management reality' and/or changing management practice to accommodate doctors' preferences. Secondly, there was a great deal of consistency about the direction of change. For all ten decisions doctors wanted to have more influence. Managers wanted a greater say in four decision areas but did express the view that they would prefer doctors to have more influence in five of the decision areas. Thirdly, the absolute difference between doctors and managers was greater in the preferred situation than the real situation for eight of the ten decisions.

These results indicate that generally there is a repelling force between doctors and managers, that is opposition or divergence, rather than a tendency towards convergence or partnership. It can also be seen that generally both managers and doctors wanted to see most change in those decisions over which they currently had least influence. For example, managers wanted most change in the direction of greater management influence in the three areas where doctors had most power, namely the appointment of consultants, prescribing policy, and the awarding of consultant merit awards.

The qualitative data from good decisions was clustered together in groups to produce construct categories. The construct categories are the key factors in distinguishing good from poor decisions (summarised in Table 3).

Table 2: Actual and preferred levels of influence

		Doctors	Managers	Doctors minus managers	Dissonance for doctors	Dissonance for managers
Strategic direction	Real	3.33	2.82	0.51		
	Preferred	2.44	2.73	−0.29	+0.88	+0.09
Resectorisation	Real	2.44	2.18	0.26		
	Preferred	1.88	2.45	−0.57	+0.55	−0.27
Service agreements	Real	3.55	4	−0.45		
	Preferred	2.88	3	−0.12	+0.66	+1
Service developments	Real	3.33	3	0.33		
	Preferred	2.22	2.73	−0.51	+1.11	+0.27
Consultant appointments	Real	1.44	1.09	0.35		
	Preferred	1.33	2.09	−0.76	+0.11	−1
Reprovision/PFI	Real	3.44	3.09	0.35		
	Preferred	2.33	3	−0.67	+1.11	+0.09
Prescribing policy	Real	1.66	1.18	0.48		
	Preferred	1.33	1.82	−0.49	+0.33	−0.64
CIP	Real	4	4	0		
	Preferred	2.77	3.18	−0.41	+1.22	+0.82
Merit awards	Real	1.66	1.36	0.3		
	Preferred	1.44	2.36	−0.92	+0.22	−1
Ward closure changes	Real	3.55	3	0.55		
	Preferred	2.33	3	−0.67	+1.22	0

Table shows mean scores

Key:
1 = Decisions made by doctors with minimal influence from managers.
2 = Decisions made by doctors with significant influence from managers.
3 = Decisions made by managers with significant influence from doctors.
4 = Decisions made by managers with minimal influence from doctors.

Dissonance = Real − Preferred.

For the last two columns   + score = Change desired towards greater doctor influence.
                            − score = Change desired towards greater manager influence.

Table 3: Construct categories

	Good decisions	Poor decisions
Communication	Dialogue	Monologue
Stakeholder involvement	Inclusion	Exclusion
Group processes	Teamwork	Independent activity
Problem solving	Learning	Repetitive
Values	Shared	Different
Leadership	Present	Weak
Outcome orientation	Analysis of consequences	Short term
Resource management	Available	Paucity

Each construct category can be seen as a continuum, for example good communication was two way and between people whereas poor communication tended to be one way. Good communication not only shared information, but also knowledge, motives and goals. Good decisions involved people whereas poor ones tended not to, or had an in-group and an out-group. Good decisions had a lot of positive group processes, that is teamwork, and poor decisions did not. Similarly there was a clear contrast between shared values and different values.

The absence of good leadership was more apparent in poor decisions – with terms used such as 'misguided' or 'lack of direction' – than the presence of good leadership reported in good decisions. Outcome orientation is a focus on understanding and evaluating the consequences of a decision, both in the longer term and with regard to its impact on others. Resource management refers to the use of resources including people and time, and consideration of implementation issues.

Are there any differences between doctors and managers? Although the numbers are small, it was found that for good decisions doctors and managers offered roughly equal contributions for four construct categories, but managers made more contributions in another four construct categories: group processes, problem solving, outcome orientation and leadership. For poor decisions, managers made far fewer references to group processes, and there was an increase in references to problem solving behaviour. These findings would support a recommendation that managers should concentrate on ensuring an effective process whilst doctors should focus on the content.

Does the trigger prompting a decision make a difference to the outcome? I identified three categories of triggers: opportunities, problems, or opportunities/problems. There was an equal distribution of these triggers between good and poor decisions. Similarly, there was no difference between good and poor decisions for the stated use or absence of an explicit systematic decision making process, or the time taken to make the decision. These could all be false-negative results because of the small sample size, but if they are of any significance it seems reasonable to conclude that the effects are significantly smaller than other factors at work.

The decision I selected for the interviews was neither a 'good decision' nor an ideal example of partnership. The specific content of the decision is relatively unimportant to this discussion – it was simply used as a case study for gathering the perspectives of doctors and managers on the same issues. To reach a decision, doctors and managers had to come together on a working party over a period of time and make recommendations about the appropriate sectors for service delivery in the future.

The construct categories in Table 3 were represented in the interviews. The issues of involvement, values, leadership and outcome orientation were very clearly present. Differences in values were seen in areas such as the degree of consensus desired, the degree of transparency of the process, and the importance of patients. It seemed also that the decision making group paid inadequate attention to analysing the consequences of the decisions taken.

In addition, the interviews were characterised by three themes – power, conflict and emotions.

The importance of power was seen within the decision making group and outside it. There were examples of this suppressing contributions and causing bias. A social structure emerges in any decision making group in which people are tacitly ranked in accordance with their status. This kind of group dynamic made an enormous difference to behaviour, with high status group members tending to dominate the group and the agenda and decisions influenced more by who was speaking than what was said.

Significant conflict was present, between doctors but not between doctors and managers. There was very little open conflict within the group, rather it festered under the surface or took place between individuals outside the formal decision making process. Several doctors acted out of self interest and the managers avoided tackling these issues, leaving the doctors to fight it out.

High emotions and a range of feelings were described that similarly required acknowledgement and effective management. This resulted either in actions to avoid conflict, which only served to delay it, or in the over-hasty adoption of an apparent solution in order to reduce anxiety – which resulted in a failure to consider the implications of the proposed 'solution'.

Interviewees and several questionnaire respondents made general comments recognising the importance of certain individuals and relationships to decision making, but indicating a wish for a 'democratic' process and greater fairness.

A model of participatory decision making

There is a whole academic discipline devoted to understanding management decision-making. Much of the literature classifies the decision-making process in stages. The diagnosis and implementation stages receive least attention in the literature, with most writing focussed on the evaluation-choice routine. In a study of diagnosis/problem formulation activities (Lyles 1981), 75% of the sample initially defined the problem incorrectly and had to redefine it, as seen in the case study.

Decision-making is also a social process, the rightness of decisions depends on whether the leader has utilised the right people in the right way. An unstructured problem where acceptance is necessary for effective implementation, where an independent decision would not be accepted by subordinates who may not share the organisational goals, indicate the use of inclusive group processes, according to Vroom and Yetton (1973), who found that decisions are far more likely to fail due to deficiencies of acceptance than due to the quality of the decision.

From the themes that emerged from my research project, and from the literature on managerial decision-making, it seems that decisions will be improved where the parties:

- Take account of the nature of power in organisations
- Understand the effects of emotion on joint decisions
- Take steps to manage conflict when it arises

There is considerable evidence that political power is a key element in decision making (Pettigrew, 1973). It is important at the problem definition stage, which is often influenced less by the facts and more by who interprets them. The implementation stage is often when defeated interests may try and recoup their losses by selective interpretation, ignoring instructions, delay and sabotage. This delay and sabotage were seen in the decision I explored in the interviews.

Decision-makers, therefore, need to understand something of the nature of power in organisations. Power is not only used to control the general decision premises, the alternatives considered, but also the information about those alternatives (Pfeffer, 1982). Since evaluation of options depends upon information, interests can potentially achieve their objectives by controlling information about alternatives. Hard data in the NHS is normally scarce, encouraging a reliance on opinion and faith in gut feelings – 'heart over head'.

All decisions are affected by emotion to some degree. Emotion becomes a problem, only when it eclipses reality. When things are going badly, fear is likely to result in undue reliance on intuition, or in a tendency to behave vindictively towards someone else, or in a desire to end the pain of indecision (Janis 1989). Emotional decisions were made in the example I investigated, where the disadvantages of chosen courses of action were ignored, no contingency plans were made, and no one stopped to consider alternative options.

The decision-maker must recognise the inevitability of conflict and the need to manage it rather than to try and avoid it. It is important to resist group pressures tempting one to yield to others without sound reasons, just in order to attain a consensus. The ability to keep an open mind to opposing views, in the words of Peter Senge (1990) for members to 'hold their position gently' is integral to team learning and synergism. Senge regards the most important characteristic as the ability to engage in dialogue. This form of communication is honest and open and is the opposite of manipulative communication characterised by deception and coercion. The salient features of dialogue are that members show genuine respect for each other, even if they disagree strongly in their views. They discuss openly the assumptions underlying their mental models and they have a common mental picture of what they are trying to achieve. In a debate, each member is attempting to defeat the other, but in dialogue they are engaged in a quest for mutual understanding. For doctors and managers to regard each other as colleagues when possible helps prevent the slippage to 'I'm right, you're wrong', and helps establish a safe atmosphere in which to take risks and keep assumptions in suspension.

Whilst acknowledging the utility of good relationships between doctors and managers, any theoretical model needs to include the construct categories identified and the other key findings. I therefore tentatively propose the theoretical model shown in Figure 1. It is inspired by the notion that learning should be central to any model seeking to improve the management of a problem to produce a better outcome, by Kolb's learning cycle and the observation that decision making is often cyclical. Pfiffner (1960) noted that the decision making process is not linear but more circular, it resembles 'the process of fermentation in biochemistry

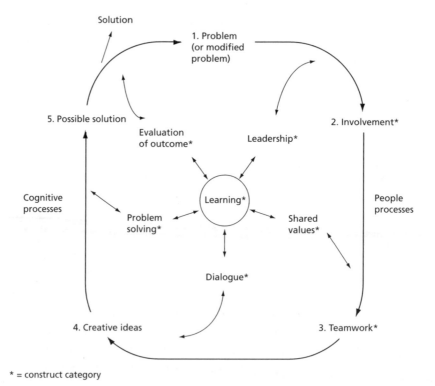

Figure 1: A theoretical model for participatory decision making

rather than the industrial assembly line'. The cyclical nature can be seen during identification in order to recognise the issue, during design to allow incubation before insight occurs, and during evaluation in order to understand the consequences of alternatives.

The stages from problem recognition, through involvement to teamwork and creating ideas and possible solutions are shown in the outer rim. The process may require one cycle or many, with the most complex decisions involving more comprehension cycles, with learning occurring with each circuit to develop understanding.

Learning is shown in the model as the hub of the wheel, with each key factor or competency – leadership, shared values, communication, problem solving and evaluating shown as spokes, where they are most critical in improving the effectiveness of the decision. Leadership and shared values are vital in involving people and producing teamwork. The leader should establish ground rules that create a culture which is open and not secretive and which values contributions. Then dialogue and problem solving are valuable in generating possible solutions. Finally, these must be evaluated if an effective outcome that meets the needs of those involved is to be achieved.

Bureaucratic chains of command have never been effective in managing doctors; managing medical consultants has been likened to herding cats. An approach based on the ideas of knowledge management is more likely to succeed and engage consultants. Clinical governance (A First Class Service, 1998) may prove to be a real opportunity to transform the doctor–manager relationship if it is designed and implemented with mutual learning as its cornerstone. The educational tradition in medicine is an invaluable asset, since doctors have always striven to be up to date in scientific knowledge and clinical practice. Indeed the knowledge and skills of clinical staff are probably the NHS's greatest asset. Bureaucratic controls depend on centralising information whereas successful working in a professional culture depends on distribution of knowledge to where it can best be used. A good information system would increase transparency of decision making and should support teamwork rather than being a weapon to use against opponents. Sadly this is not yet feasible in a NHS with a very inadequate IT system.

Doctors and managers are interdependent and must co-operate by mutual adjustment as partners in a joint venture. They have different attitudes, knowledge and skills, but the challenge is to manage those differences in order to maximise effectiveness. They must learn together, using such concepts as intellectual capital and clinical governance, if sustainable development of the NHS is to be achieved.

References

Department of Health (1998) *A First Class Service: Quality in the New NHS.* London.

Glaser, B.G.& Strauss, A. (1967) *The discovery of grounded theory: strategies for qualitative research.* Chicago. Aldine.

Harrison, S; Hunter, D.J.; Marnoch, G. & Pollitt, C. (1992) *Just Managing: Power and Culture in the National Health Service.* Macmillan.

Janis, I. (1989) *Crucial Decisions: Leadership in Policy Making and Crisis Management.* Free Press.

Lyles, M.A. (1981) Formulating strategic problems. *Strategic Management Journal.* 12: 61–75.

Pettigrew, A.M. (1973) *The Politics of Organisational Decision Making.* Tavistock.

Pfeffer, J. (1982) *Power in Organisations.* Pitman.

Pfiffner, J.M. (1960) Administrative rationality. *Public Administration Review.* 125–132.

Senge, P.M. (1990) *The Fifth Discipline.* Century Business.

Vroom, V.H. & Yetton, P.W. (1973) *Leadership and Decision-Making.* University of Pittsburgh Press.

■ Tony Dearden is currently a Consultant Psychiatrist and the Associate Medical Director (Old Age Psychiatry) Leeds Community and Mental Health Services (Teaching) NHS Trust.

CHAPTER THIRTEEN

Social distance in leadership

Martin Jones

Introduction

The subject of distance in leader–follower relationships has always intrigued me. Central to this have been questions such as: Is it wise for leaders to adopt a formal approach so that difficult decisions can be taken when the need arises? Can leaders develop close relationships, even friendships with those they lead without compromising their impartiality? Do followers want leaders to be friendly, or would they prefer some distance in relationships?

The aim of my research was to gain a better insight into the factors that determine how close or distant leaders become in relationships. The essence of social distance is perhaps encapsulated in the work of Boccialetti (1996) who considered distance in terms of whether relationships are personalised or whether a more role-oriented approach is adopted.

The use of terms such as leaders and followers in the NHS is not without problem. Leadership and management are different processes. Managerial or leadership texts tend to associate leadership with change. The leader's role is one of recognising the need for change, setting a new direction and motivating followers to work towards a shared view of the future. Management on the other hand is seen as being concerned with control and the reduction of uncertainty and inconsistency (Bennis and Nanus 1997, Kotter 1990).

Many individuals in the NHS will undertake a combination of both processes and the notion that a single group of staff might be highlighted as leaders and others as followers is not so straightforward. Bartolomé and Laurent (1986) point out that managers often have a duality in the leader–follower relationship, in that they both have staff who report to them and in turn have their own superiors to whom they report. In one situation they can be called upon to act as leader, whilst in another they may act as a follower. This duality is not confined to those carrying the title 'manager' and can apply in the case of staff in their own spheres of responsibility. For the purpose of this study I will equate the process of leadership with managers who have an organisational leadership role. Rather than adopt the terminology 'leaders' and 'followers', which I feel sits rather uncomfortably in the NHS, I will henceforth use the terms 'managers' and 'staff'.

My interest in undertaking this research was both personal and organisational. First, from a personal perspective I was interested in gaining a better understanding of the factors that influence my own predominant behaviour and to understand more about the consequences of this. Secondly, from an organisational perspective, I was interested in understanding more about those factors that might either facilitate or inhibit relationships. Clearly, in terms of leading innovation and change the nature of relationships can be an important determinant of the success or otherwise of change initiatives.

I consider my own predominant behaviour to be approachable, but formal. Indeed, I might even be described as a traditionalist. I would not consider it particularly healthy to develop close relationships at work, as I believe that there is a potential for this to cloud objectivity and make it more awkward to be involved in difficult decisions involving those people with whom I had a close relationship. I mention this because, whilst every effort was made to exclude personal bias, I recognise that we all have deep-seated values and beliefs that may colour the way we view the world. This might unwittingly be of significance in the way the research was constructed and the findings interpreted.

Research

A literature search identified six main factors that might influence the distance maintained in manager–staff relationships at work, as set out in Table 1.

The aim of the research was to offer insight and plausible explanation, rather than test a theory or create a new theory from observations. As such, the theoretical perspective was that of the social constructionist.

Table 1: Factors influencing the distance maintained in manager–staff relationships

Factor	Sources
Self protection and objectivity	Adair (1998), Kanter (1988), Fiedler – cited in Handy (1993)
Organisational culture – including the example set by the Board and the Chief Executive	Goffee and Jones (1998), Kotter and Heskett (1992), Garratt (1996), Burns and Stalker (1996)
Role conflict	Pugh, (1978), Krantz (1989)
Power differentials	Handy (1993), Bartolomé and Laurent (1986)
Managerial style	Boccialetti (1996), Hersey and Blanchard (1993), Burns – cited in Boak and Thompson (1998)
Psychodynamics – the influence of early life experiences of both leaders and followers	Kotter (1988), Krantz (1989), Stech (1997)

I carried out a survey, using a self-completion questionnaire. The questionnaire was designed in three parts. In part one, two factual items were sought; gender and length of time working for the Trust or its predecessor organisations. In part two, eighteen statements were given against which respondents were asked to detail whether they agreed or disagreed against a four-option scale. These statements reflected factors identified in the literature search. Part three of the questionnaire consisted of three open-ended questions.

The research was undertaken at a 500+ bed District General Hospital serving the needs of a mainly rural area. For the purpose of this study, the population of managers was taken as the twenty-five hospital based managers on the senior manager's distribution list. In the case of the staff survey, names were obtained from attendance lists from three fire lectures. These were held at various times to ensure access by early, late and night shifts. Forty-one names were obtained. The staff chosen by this sampling did not necessarily relate directly to those managers included in the survey.

Findings

The questionnaire enlisted a good response – 76% for senior managers and 82% from staff. There was no discernible difference in the response rates from male or female participants.

Table 2: Length of service of respondents

	Mean length of service (years)	Median length of service (years)
Managers	15	16
Female managers	16	16
Male managers	14	16
Staff	11	9

Respondents had a long length of service with the Trust or its predecessor organisations, as shown in Table 2.

This stability in the workforce could be a factor in determining the distances maintained as managers and staff build up relationships over an extended period of time.

There was little evidence, from the analysis of the responses to the eighteen statements in part two of the questionnaire, to suggest that self-protection, role conflict, cultural aspects or psychodynamics played a significant part in determining the distance maintained. Managerial style and differentials in power were identified as being important.

Both managers and staff identified personal style as the main determinant of distance. Both agreed that the style adopted stemmed from a wish to get close to staff to appreciate details of their outside interests and family life, although managers were more inclined to this view than were staff. Female managers claimed a greater knowledge about the families and outside interests of those they manage than did male managers and they were more inclined to believe that close friendship with staff was compatible with their managerial role. Both managers and staff agreed that distance is as much a reflection of staff expectations as it is of those of managers. Managers did not tend to socialise outside work with those they manage and interestingly staff did not feel that managers should do so.

Whilst both managers and staff agreed that power differentials arise from the organisational structure, there were differences of opinion as to whether this results in staff keeping a distance. When personalised, however, managers did not feel that staff kept a distance from them due to differences in power. Staff on the other hand, said that they did maintain a certain distance from managers due to differences in power. Female managers were more inclined to acknowledge the impact of power differentials than were male managers and they appeared more ready to acknowledge the influence of systems and structures, which can perhaps be considered as manifestations of power.

The open ended questions in part 3 of the questionnaire provided staff with an opportunity to be more open and expansive in sharing their views. Each response was sub-divided into meaning units, each of which was allocated a unique identifier. Whilst individual statements or elements can provide insight in their own right, this qualitative data can be transformed into quantitative information by grouping items and expressing the frequency of occurrence. The main factor identified by managers was management behaviour focused on a desire to show respect for and trust in staff. Staff identified a more practical issue, that of time available for managers and staff to get to know one another. They added to this by highlighting factors around accessibility to managers and regular contact.

Both managers (64%) and staff (77%) believed that the distance maintained in relationships is affected by whether managers like or dislike staff. Respondents offered a number of practical consequences of preferences. Managers focused on factors aimed at ensuring consistency and fairness – additional attention to ensure that the views of all staff were heard, a tendency to over-compensate and put up with poor performance and special attention to persons with whom they had difficulty communicating. Staff on the other hand showed a strong tendency to highlight negative aspects of preferences – favouritism towards those liked and poor working relationships with those disliked.

The theme of favouritism was particularly strong and brought out some powerful comments, such as those detailed below.

> 'They are more likely to help those they have friendships with more than those they have not'

> 'Like or dislike is reflected in favouritism. Individuals are quite openly treated in a different manner and with more respect if they are liked'

> 'Yes I fear favouritism is rife within the department as to why I'm at a loss. Maybe, its because the manager likes the person they've chosen through interview and sticks with them no matter what they do or they hold grudges for some reason'

Respondents offered a number of comments when given an opportunity to make general observations on the subject of manager–staff relationships. These included:

> 'Close friendships can work so long as both parties know the demarcation line. Always useful to have outside influences as well as friendship within work so as to get balanced view'
>
> Contribution by female manager

> 'It is more difficult for a manager to keep distance if they have risen "through the ranks" rather than being appointed into a senior post from outside the organisation (they don't owe favours or have loyalties to anybody)'
>
> Contribution by member of staff

> 'The nature of the hierarchy within the Trust from senior nursing staff to executive members cultivates distance between managers and staff. I do not feel that this is particularly damaging but is unfavourable in such large organisations'
>
> Contribution by member of staff

Mapping of the meaning units identified many of the factors highlighted earlier. Managers identified the importance of managerial behaviour aimed at respect, trust and honesty in dealings with staff and the importance of good communication skills. Whilst staff also highlighted the importance of managerial behaviour, they once again strongly identified the importance of accessibility and the need for consistency and lack of favouritism.

Implications

In leading innovation and change, those leading should be aware that followers might suppress their true feelings and opinions, due to a concern about the power differences between their respective positions. Whilst followers might verbalise agreement to a course of action, their actual feelings may be the opposite. This could manifest itself in unanticipated resistance to change.

Of particular note is the evidence that senior managers, whilst recognising that the structure of the organisation creates power differences, do not recognise that this applies in their personal dealings with staff. This equates well with the findings of Bartolomé and Laurent (1986). As part of the process of ensuring validity, the results of this survey were shared with several senior managers at the Trust. A number found the discussion on power differences and their possible consequence particularly thought provoking. Whilst these managers believed that they were approachable, they admitted that they might not personally share all their true feelings with their superiors. When asked why they thought that their staff should feel comfortable sharing all their feelings with them as a manager, when they themselves were not totally honest and open with their superiors, all acknowledged that their self-perception of their approachability might be misplaced.

Whilst the evidence supports staff maintaining a certain distance due to concerns about differences in power, there was also evidence to suggest that staff were receptive to developing a better understanding of managers. Several references were made to the absence of appropriate time to get to know one another, difficulty with accessibility of managers and regular contact.

Both managers and staff agree that personal style is a major factor in how close managers get to staff. There is general agreement that managers get close to staff to understand their values and concerns, and there is evidence of an interest in the families and outside activities of those they manage. Managers suggest that the distance they maintain from staff is determined by respect for, interest in and honesty towards staff. It would appear that the predominant style in operation at the hospital is participative in the sense that there is evidence of attention being given to the interests of staff. This is not to say that a focus on relationships takes precedent over organisational objectives. Both managers and staff suggest that it is the reverse.

Whilst I have previously identified myself as a traditionalist who maintains some distance in social relationships with staff, the decision as to what is appropriate for individuals is clearly multi-faceted. Those charged with leadership in organisations should be prepared to accept that others in the organisation may adopt positions in which they are closer or more distant from staff, reflecting their personal makeup, the attitude of their staff and the particular circumstances of the area in which they operate.

There was some evidence from the responses from male and female managers that there might be a gender difference in the distance maintained and the style adopted. Female managers appear more accepting that friendship with staff is compatible with their management role. They appear to be more sensitive to the influence of power differences, policies and procedures and appear to take a greater interest in the families and outside activities of those they manage. Male managers on the other hand were more inclined to feel that friendship was not compatible with their management role and they were also more inclined to believe that managers and staff have different expectations and behaviours. Several authors (Alimo-Metcalfe (1995), Bass et al (1996)) consider there to be a gender difference in leadership style, with women being more inclined to a transformational approach. Other such as Goleman (1998) argue that research suggests that male and female managers have as much latent ability for such factors as empathy, but male managers are less likely to use it for they perceive this to be a weakness. There is insufficient evidence within this research to conclude that the style adopted by female managers is more transformational, but the greater sensitivity of female managers to control mechanisms and interest in staff suggest that this might be so.

Whatever style adopted by managers, there appears to be a clear warning about the need for consistency. More importantly it is consistency in the eyes of staff, rather than in the eyes of the manager. This research obtained numerous comments alluding to perceived problems with favouritism. It is not possible to say whether these allegations were true or just perceived, but clearly perceived favouritism can create tension that might cause resistance to change. If close relationships are preferred, then it is important that it applies in the case of all staff otherwise there is a risk that this might be construed or misconstrued as favouritism. Given human nature, and the tendency to like certain individuals more than others, this may be difficult to achieve.

Bibliography

Adair, J. (1998) *Effective Leadership* London: Pan.

Alimo-Metcalfe, B. (1995) 'An investigation of female and male constructs of leadership and empowerment' *Women in Management Review* 10: 2 pp. 3–8.

Bartolomé, F. & Laurent, A. (1986) 'The Manager: master and servant of power' *Harvard Business Review* Vol. 64 No. 6 November – December pp. 77–81.

Bass, B.M., Avilo, B.J. & Atwater, L. (1996) 'The transformational and transactional leadership of men and women' *Applied Psychology: an International review* Vol. 45, No 1 pp. 5–34.

Bennis, W and Nanus, B (1997) *Leaders,* London: Harper Business.

Boak, G. & Thompson, D. (1998) *Mental Models for Managers* London: Century

Boccialetti, G. (1996) 'Making authority relationships reciprocal' *Training and Development* (USA) Vol. 50 No. 6 June pp. 35–40.

Burns, T. & Stalker, G.M. (1996) *The Management of Innovation* Oxford: Oxford University Press.

Garratt, B. (1996) *The fish rots from the head* London: Harper Collins.

Goffee, R & Jones, G. (1998) *The Character of a Corporation* London: Harper Collins.

Goleman, D. (1998) *Working with Emotional Intelligence* London: Bloomsbury.

Handy, C. (1993) *Understanding organisations* London: Penguin.

Hersey, P. & Blanchard, K.H. (1993) *Management of Organizational Behaviour* New Jersey: Prentice-Hall.

Kanter, R.M. (1988) *The Change Masters* London: Thomson.

Kotter, J.P. (1988) *The Leadership Factor* New York: Free Press.

Kotter, J.P. (1990) *A Force for Change* New York: Free Press.

Kotter, J.P. & Heskett, J.L. (1992) *Corporate culture and performance.*

Krantz, J. (1989) 'The Managerial Couple: Superior-Subordinate Relationships as a Unit of Analysis'. *Human Resource Management* Summer Vol. 28, No 2 pp. 161–175.

Pugh, D. (1978) 'Role activation conflict: a study of industrial inspection'. In G.Salaman & K. Thompson (Eds) *People and Organisations* London: Longman.

Stech, E.L. (1997) 'Psychodynamic approach'. In P.G. Northouse *Leadership – Theory and Practice* London: Sage.

■ Martin Jones is an Executive Director of Operations and Performance Management at a Welsh NHS Trust. A career manager by background, he has held several posts at acute hospitals and Trusts in both Wales and in the Midlands, England.

CHAPTER FOURTEEN

Towards Clinical Governance

Mike Porte

Introduction

This chapter, on clinical governance and its implementation revolves around changing a theoretical concept into a practical reality. As part of my study for the MA in Leading Innovation and Change, I analysed the approach to this in my Trust, using an action research methodology, and incorporating some depth interviews. For this chapter I have selected certain points of the process, in the hope that they will provide illumination, or at least spark some recognition, among fellow clinical leaders.

I work in a large combined acute and community NHS trust employing over 5000 staff. The operating core of the trust is arranged into functional directorates, such as general surgery or medicine. The work of the directorates is coordinated by a management structure comprising of the trust board, general managers and their support staff.

I was appointed Medical Director of my Trust in June 1999, and began my duties the following September. In the majority of Trusts, including ours, the chief executive delegated responsibility for clinical governance to the medical director. In a sense, this chapter is about how I made sense (rather slowly) of the idea of clinical governance and made some progress in putting it into practice.

The concept of Clinical Governance

After 18 years in opposition a new Labour government came to power in May 1997 with a wealth of new ideas and energy to drive them through. Rapid action was seen in areas such as transport, education and devolution. In opposition, Labour made political capital by opposing the Tory

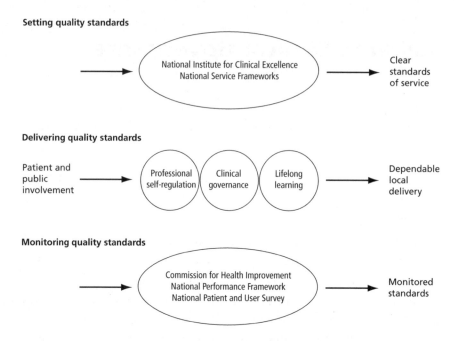

Setting quality standards

National Institute for Clinical Excellence
National Service Frameworks

Clear
standards
of service

Delivering quality standards

Patient and
public
involvement

Professional
self-regulation

Clinical
governance

Lifelong
learning

Dependable
local
delivery

Monitoring quality standards

Commission for Health Improvement
National Performance Framework
National Patient and User Survey

Monitored
standards

Figure 1: Delivering quality standards in clinical care

health service reforms, especially the internal market. Against this background the lack of reform of the Health Service was an obvious anomaly.

Eventually, the much leaked White Paper 'The New NHS: modern, dependable,' (1997) was released, and its broad themes for change were given more substance in the consultation document 'A First Class Service: Quality in the NHS' (1998), which first introduced the model to deliver quality standards in clinical care, as shown in Figure 1.

Clinical governance sits at the heart of the model and is supposed to be the lynchpin which ensures quality of care in the new NHS. The accompanying text defines clinical governance as:

> A framework through which NHS organisations are accountable for continuously improving the quality of their services and safeguarding high standards of care by creating an environment in which excellence in clinical care will flourish.

This document outlines the strategy for implementation of clinical governance, detailing four key steps to be undertaken in the first year as follows:

- Establish leadership, accountability and working arrangements.
- Carry out a baseline assessment of capacity and capability.
- Formulate and agree a development plan in the light of this assessment.
- Clarify reporting arrangements for clinical governance within Board and Annual Reports.

The Medical Director

I became the Medical Director at the Trust in September 1999. My predecessor was a full time medical director. When he announced his retirement there was great debate as to whether the post should be part, or full time. I was amongst those who supported a part time appointment, the espoused reason being the need to act as a bridge between the executives of the trust and the clinical core of the organisation. Fortunately, I felt this to be true but I also knew that I could only accept the job on a part time basis as this was the only way to maintain my clinical skills, a necessary insurance for a young man moving into the insecure world of medical management.

Moving into this new leadership role prompted some reflection on my own capabilities as a leader. A strength I felt I brought to the role was an ability to see the bigger picture, and to develop creative solutions to challenging problems. I knew that my preferred style of leadership was not participative, or particularly collaborative, pushing me towards the autocratic end of the continuum of styles. I partly fit Belbin's description of a 'Shaper' – an energetic, task-orientated leader, with a clear focus on achieving results, although I did not relish conflict in the way that seems to me implied in the description of such a leader, and indeed I tended to be quick to resort to compromise and accommodation when conflict arose.

This preferred style had been refined in the political culture rife among doctors, but I recognised it was not wholly appropriate to my new role. As Medical Director, I wanted to bridge the gap between the medical culture and the more bureaucratic culture that unsurprisingly existed at the top of such a large organisation. The only logical conclusion was that I would have to adapt my preferred leadership style, and become much more open and participative. I realised I must accept, as Mintzberg (1989) says, that conflict can be healthy, that compromise is sometimes appeasement, and that open debate can change ideas for the better and the very process leads to ownership of those ideas by a team.

The implementation of Clinical Governance

As part of my appointment process I was asked to write a paper on the potential of Clinical Governance for my Trust. I had read the seminal government documents, and my predecessor's assessment of the Trust's baseline capability, but this was the first time I had put pen to paper on this subject. Re-reading my paper now it is obvious that I had no clear idea what clinical governance entailed. I blended recycled parts of the White Paper with hazy ideas and noble concepts into a rather unedifying whole.

My lack of understanding of my key responsibility genuinely frightened me such that I was awake in the early hours of most nights with worry. At the time the Trust was without a chief executive, and the remainder of the management team were overburdened and preoccupied. I could also feel myself becoming distanced from my clinical colleagues.

The previous medical director had spent a great deal of time and energy trying to crystallise the structure to support clinical governance within the Trust. I was happy to continue the debate as structures were something concrete that I understood. My proposals of alternatives at least gave the appearance of activity. In fact there was a major unanswered question around the clinical governance structure, namely how did it relate to the rest of the organisational structure? Without strong links into the rest of the organisation, the clinical governance structure was in danger of functioning in a vacuum. Its outputs could be excellent but would be ignored.

Important though these structural issues were, they were also a convenient distraction. A monthly clinical governance report was expected by the trust board and that month's latest version of the structure formed a prominent part in these early months. The remainder of the report would highlight one or more topics relevant to clinical governance. These were found by asking people such as the head of the clinical effectiveness unit, the director of nursing, or the post graduate tutor whether they had anything to contribute that month. In this way I was able to address structural issues whilst simultaneously demonstrating outputs. The trust board were happy but I was not. I knew that I had to address the central question of what did clinical governance actually mean to our organisation? At this time I referred to clinical governance as the latter day Yeti. It was big, probably had large teeth and was out there somewhere although no one actually knew what it looked like.

A simple view of how strategy is made at the top of large organisations is that rational, long-term plans are made which contain clear goals and milestones. Alternatively, Mintzberg and Waters (1985) place theories of how strategy is formulated along a continuum from pure deliberate strategies – such as the rational plan – to what they term purely 'emergent strategies' – strategies which arise without any deliberate intent on the part of the 'strategy makers'.

Mintzberg and Waters also make the powerful point that however deliberate the intended strategy (the plan) the final realised strategy (what the organisation actually does) may be very different. Firstly part or all of an intended strategy may be unrealised and secondly, new strategies may emerge from within the organisation to modify the original intent.

Mintzberg and Waters contend that the poles of pure deliberate and pure emergent strategies are rare. Most strategies lie somewhere along the continuum in between. Close to the centre of their spectrum they place what they term the 'umbrella strategy'. In this, managers have a good idea of the overall direction of travel of the organisation but emergent strategies are also tolerated. If these emergent strategies fit with the overall direction of travel, well and good, but if they are at variance with overall plans a decision must be made. Either the emergent strategy must be eliminated or the strategic vision of the organisation must be readjusted. Mintzberg and Waters contend both that this model is common in real life, and that the tension created by dissonant emergent strategies is a positive process for organisational learning and adaptation to its environment.

There were strong elements of emergent strategy in how we proceeded with Clinical Governance in the Trust, and I would like to illustrate this by describing three critical incidents which helped to shape events.

Enlightenment

I suffered from a lack of a clear vision of what we trying to achieve with clinical governance, and the fact that I was new to the job meant that I did not have a strong grip on strategy formulation processes within the Trust. I kept my lack of knowledge and confusion to myself, but I was acutely aware that I was failing to progress the clinical governance agenda. This was an overwhelmingly stressful period. I felt I was reacting to events rather than controlling them.

I attended a conference on clinical governance that provided the revelation I needed to break out of this situation. At the conference, a series of speakers stood up and said that they did not understand clinical governance. Each spent the following hour proving their opening statement. It was clear that most managers and senior clinicians were as confused as I was. Only then was it obvious that the concept itself, and all the associated guidance, was confused in its goals and unclear as to its method of implementation.

I realised that we had never agreed what actually constituted clinical governance for us as an organisation. The concept is like an onion or a Russian doll, with many layers, one upon another. Unless clinical governance, and most importantly its boundaries are defined, it is simply a catch-all phrase to be used or ignored as required. I decided my task was to ensure that there was widespread agreement around a clear definition. Within reason, what the definition actually said was of lesser importance.

The scope of Clinical Governance

The conference provided a huge release for me. It gave me the confidence to sit down and write my own definition of what clinical governance meant locally. My intention was to break the concept down into its constituent parts such that each part could be evaluated, monitored and developed. The danger inherent in a local definition is that it will simply overlook a key constituent part of clinical governance. Equally importantly, however the definition was reached, it had to be agreed and owned by the key members of the organisation.

I presented a paper, 'The Scope of Clinical Governance' to the Clinical Standards Executive (CSE). I asked its members to read and comment on it as they saw fit but at least to answer the specific questions, did they approve of the overall approach? Also, had I missed anything out? I promised to revise the document in the light of their comments, several times if necessary, in order to produce an agreed working document.

I felt secure enough to put forward my proposals now that I recognised the general difficulty in defining clinical governance, rather than fearing my difficulties were due to personal lack of understanding.

Many authors speak of change in terms of a series of steps. Lewin (1951) for example, described three steps of unfreezing, shaping and refreezing. Although the model is flawed because it regards change as a discontinuous process, with a beginning, middle and end, it does provide a useful mental framework. My paper was designed to represent the unfreezing stage of the change process. I felt that this was the point in the change process where my talents lie – challenging existing ideas and practices. It was therefore a most unpleasant surprise when I received some very negative feedback on my paper. Conflict may be healthy for the strategy-making process, but I still felt very uncomfortable being on the receiving end of criticism.

The ensuing debate was very useful, centring around the differences between monitoring a process and controlling a process. It became obvious that the role of our clinical governance structure should be to monitor internal processes and to assess their quality. It had to rely on its links with other parts of the organisation to make any changes necessary as it did not have the capacity to do so itself. Also, it would be wrong to try to allow the clinical governance structure to control processes as the result would be two competing structures. It was vital to the success of clinical governance that it fed its views into the pre-existing management structure rather than inventing a new competing bureaucracy.

I reworked the paper and involved my most vocal critic in the rewrite and gained general acceptance of the revised version.

As a result, we had an agreed framework – an umbrella strategy – for what actually constitutes clinical governance within our organisation. Each new initiative or idea either fits into the framework or, if it does not, the question is whether it is part of the clinical governance agenda or does the framework require adjustment? I saw this process of questioning as a vital mechanism to ensure that clinical governance is continuously evolving and improving within the trust.

Questions and conclusions

The third critical incident, which had a significant effect on how I feel we should approach Clinical Governance in the Trust, was controversial, with a number of competing interpretations.

We collect a huge, and ever increasing, amount of data on clinical activity, including death rates by operation type. My predecessor was shown information showing that twice as many of one surgeon's patients died after a particular complex procedure than those of his colleagues. He shared this information with the surgeons and asked the clinical effectiveness unit to perform a further audit to confirm or refute the findings. The relevant surgeon stopped performing some of the more complex procedures. A prospective audit was then performed which showed no difference in outcomes whoever performed the surgery.

The clinical effectiveness unit looked at the initial retrospective data and found that it was statistically valid. The surgeons looked at the same data and found innumerable errors such as wrong patient or wrong surgeon, in their eyes, invalidating the data.

Hostility between the surgeons and the clinical effectiveness unit escalated, and generated much heat as well as (eventually) light. I was drawn into the situation when both parties looked to me for a resolution. By talking to the protagonists together, going over the data and the surrounding events, I was able to get each to concede there was some truth in the position of the other party. A prospective audit was agreed. The input data was to be validated by the surgeons before it was processed by the clinical effectiveness unit.

As well as wishing to resolve the immediate problem, I regarded it as vital that both I, and the organisation learnt from the episode.

I concluded that the way forward was to ensure that all the key stakeholders were represented in the clinical governance structure. This would not stop disputes arising, nor would it narrow down our views to a single perspective, but it would give protagonists a forum for early debate and the permission to do so.

I also reflected upon the angry exchange of words, written and spoken, between the parties. One accusation, levelled against the clinical effectiveness unit, struck a particular chord. To quote, *'You have trawled the data in an unfocused manner in order to jump to conclusions'.*

This single phrase unwittingly captured all that is good and bad about clinical governance. It is right and proper that the data should be trawled in an unfocused manner. The mistake that was made was to jump to conclusions. What should have happened was we *should* have trawled the data in an unfocused manner but in order to ask *questions*. Once questions are raised we can focus in, reflect, perform further audit or statistical work, whatever is necessary to reach valid conclusions.

An open and honest approach to clinical practice is a vital component of clinical governance whilst the use of information to condemn staff or organisations is its greatest danger.

As a direct result of reflecting upon this phrase, a quarterly clinical data set is produced for each directorate, ranging from simple activity information, through adverse incident reports to legal claims. This data is sent without a covering gloss. The directorates can use it as they see fit but the clinical standards executive will receive the data for all the directorates. Its members will be expected to review the data and ask questions. In this way, two levels of the organisation will review all clinical data. The members of the clinical directorates have the knowledge to ask the really searching questions which will allow us to get the best from the data. The CSE is an organisational safety net to guard against the rare clinician who deliberately ignores important information.

The data should always be used to ask questions rather than to reach premature, and potentially invalid conclusions.

Conclusions

The emergent nature of clinical governance, both in its conception and its implementation, has been a key theme of this short story. As ideas about the concept formed, a strategy began to emerge but as Mintzberg and Waters (1985) show, some intended strategy is never realised whilst new strategies emerge unintended. Despite this, once I formed an overall view of the way forward it was possible to pursue an umbrella strategy, moving towards a broadly defined goal.

I am convinced that this process was absolutely inevitable given the different perspectives of key groups and individuals. Indeed, in one respect my key task was to recognise that many views of the reality of clinical governance existed.

References

Belbin, R.M. (1981) *Management Teams* Heinemann.

Lewin, K. (1951) *Field Theory in Social Science* Harper.

Mintzberg, H. (1989) *Mintzberg on Management* London: The Free Press.

Mintzberg H., and Waters, J. (1985) 'Of strategies, deliberate and emergent' *Strategic Management Journal* Vol 6 No 3.

■ Mike Porte is the Medical Director of York Health Services NHS Trust. He started medical school in 1976, became a houseman in 1982 and was appointed a consultant radiologist in 1992. At present, he says, he strives to remain optimistic through challenging times.

CHAPTER FIFTEEN

Creating new organisations – NHS Direct and NHS Professionals

Jayne Barnes

Introduction

On 9 December 1997 Mr Frank Dobson, Secretary of State for Health published the NHS White Paper 'A Modern and Dependable NHS for the Next Century'. This outlined a ten-year programme of modernisation to deliver quicker, high quality services to patients. Included in this modernisation programme was the innovative development and implementation of NHS Direct – the 24-hour advice line operated by nurses.

NHS Professionals is a national scheme to arrange temporary staffing solutions for the NHS, thus reducing reliance on commercial agency providers. It was launched by the Prime Minister Mr Tony Blair at the Chief Nursing Officers Conference in Brighton in October 2000, where he cited my organisation, WYMAS, as the model of good practice to follow.

I was involved in the development of NHS Direct in Wakefield from the beginning, and saw NHS Professionals grow from the germ of an idea into a national organisation with Prime Ministerial support. In this paper I'd like to describe some of the challenges of developing these new organisations and suggest what we need to do in order to lead innovation and change in the health service.

NHS Direct and NHS Professionals

First a brief word of explanation for readers who are not familiar with these two organisations.

NHS Direct in Wakefield began operating on 7 April 1999 in a modern building on a new industrial estate just off the M1 between Leeds and

Wakefield in West Yorkshire and currently employs approximately 100 nurses who are supported by Health Information Staff and Call Handlers.

The core service is telephone triage, using a highly technical IT and telecom approach. It's available twenty-four hours a day. Anyone who is feeling unwell can call NHS Direct and talk to a trained nurse about their symptoms.

The service is protocol-driven. Based on the caller's symptoms, the nurse can call up the appropriate protocol – or algorithm – on their computer screen and through a sequence of questions establish whether the caller can best treat themselves, or whether they should go to their GP or to their local hospital. The protocols are based on evidence derived from research, and have been thoroughly tested. The nurses have all received special training to work with the software and how to relate to patients over the telephone. If they need further help they can talk to the Medical Director on site. All calls are taped so they can be audited on a regular basis for Clinical Governance and Clinical Supervision.

This core service is now developing into other areas – including

- providing an out-of- hours cover service for GPs
- providing a monitoring service of vulnerable people in their own homes, for social services
- providing home-based tele-medicine. Through tele-medicine, we can check the patient's blood pressure and their pulse in the comfort of their own home, thus reducing the need for admission to hospital.

NHS Professionals began as an attempt to use the same technology as NHS Direct to organise a nurse bank to fill temporary vacancies. Most hospitals have an internal nurse bank system, some work well and some not. At the time I started the scheme, in two local trusts, the gap between supply and demand was growing and reliance on the commercial agencies was becoming greater.

Two years on and the service has developed incredibly, providing services to six of the eight NHS regions in England, and covering not only nurses, but also doctors and other health care professionals.

How can we lead innovation and change?

There are some lessons about leading innovation and change I've drawn from my experiences with these two organisations. These are by no means final conclusions, because I continue to learn, but they are firm enough at this time to share.

What do we need to do, in order to be effective in innovating and changing the health service?

Seven main points stand out, which I can illustrate from my own experiences.

1. Take opportunities when they arise. Make opportunities when you can.

In 1998 the Government was issuing invitations to tender for second-wave pilot sites for NHS Direct. I was interested in NHS Direct because the concept was at the leading edge of innovation. At that time it had only been piloted on a very small scale and it was a new challenge for nursing.

The service also appealed to me as a working mother, in two different ways. First, my daughter was four years old and I liked the fact that NHS Direct could provide reliable healthcare advice when my child appeared ill at night, without my having to worry about calling my GP unnecessarily. Secondly, I could see how NHS Direct could offer flexible employment to mothers of young children and nurses with other family commitments.

At the time the invitation to tender was issued, I was Executive Nurse Director in a local Trust. Unfortunately the Trust was in the process of a major Private Finance Initiative and it was inappropriate to try to take on a major new project, such as bidding to run the NHS Direct service.

I discovered that the Chief Executive of WYMAS (the West Yorkshire Metropolitan Ambulance Service) was putting together a bid for the service, so I contacted him, and offered my support in writing the bid, as a professional nurse. He welcomed this suggestion and we created a successful bid together.

With NHS Professionals, the idea came about following a conversation with my chief executive. He was complaining about the widespread problem of nurse staffing shortages, and I said that I thought I could run a national nurse bank that would solve the problem. He liked this idea and this became the start of the development of NHS Professionals.

At this time, the local hospital was reviewing its internal nurse bank arrangements because the bank co-ordinator was leaving. I spoke to the Director of Nursing there, and he agreed to become my first pilot site.

The Secretary of State for Health came to open NHS Direct in Wakefield in April 1999, and I took the opportunity to mention to him what we were doing. He passed this information on to Downing Street, and evidently suggested they keep an eye on us, to see how we developed. About a year later there was a phone call, and then a visit, and then more meetings, which led to the launch of NHS Professionals in October 2000.

I think there are still opportunities to be taken. The Government very much wants to make the NHS more effective, and they are interested in hearing from people within the service about ideas that can help that happen.

2. Do your homework

Creating both new organisations has taken a lot of preparatory work. In August 1998 we were informed our bid to run NHS Direct in Wakefield had been successful. From that point until I joined the organisation full time, in December, I worked for WYMAS a couple of days a week, with a business director, planning and scheduling how we would operate the service.

At the start of running the nurse bank at the local hospital, we did our homework by carrying out some research around flexible working. Why did nurses choose to work in this way? Why did they choose to work for a commercial agency? We also carried out some research with ward managers about what they were looking for in the bank nurses that came to work for them. This enabled us to create a service that was attractive from the outset.

Another example of thorough homework is the preparation that has gone into the protocols the nurses use in NHS Direct. They are based on software that was developed in America, which is evidence-based, but they have also been validated for use in the UK. Then we held local forums with GPs, consultants, other medics and health care professionals. We went through every protocol and we made sure it was right for this local area.

Sometimes thorough preparation means hiring the right expertise for your team. We employed someone at a senior level at Wakefield with a lot of experience in the private sector call centre industry, and that has been a tremendous appointment. She was performance-orientated and quality-orientated, with an excellent knowledge of IT and telecoms. We were the first NHS Direct site to appoint a call centre manager – but every site has them now.

3. Set the vision

It's really important to set a vision for what you want to achieve.

My chief executive set a very clear vision for NHS Direct when I first started working with him. He was the chief executive of the ambulance service here, and he had just won the contract to provide NHS Direct. He said he saw himself as the CEO of a service that had multiple facets to it – only one of which was providing transport. In other words, he didn't see NHS Direct as being a bolt-on to the ambulance service but as an integral part.

We see ourselves as supporting all the other parts of the NHS, as being the glue that can help to hold it all together. This vision has created a platform for development and continues to be as important today as it was in the beginning.

A key part of my job in the early days was to set up the organisation, to deliver the service. I had studied learning organisations, as described by Pedler and Senge, as part of my master's degree, and I wanted this organisation to have at least some of the excellent attributes of a learning organisation, so we could do things differently, create new roles, and help staff to develop to their full potential – whatever that potential is. That's still part of my vision for this organisation.

With NHS Professionals, we had discovered some really interesting things from our early research, and that helped to shape the vision for the service.

We found that pay was important to the nurses who worked on a temporary basis for nurse banks, but the main attraction to them was the flexibility of being able to say when they wanted to work, and to choose where to work. The main reason they went to a commercial agency was because of higher rates of pay and the fact they were paid on a weekly basis. But most of them made the point that if the NHS paid weekly and treated temporary workers equally, they'd rather work for the NHS.

The ward managers – who employ temporary nurses – wanted nurses who could work at the level and skill set that was required. They felt aggrieved that at times they were paying trained nurse prices for people who were only able to function at health care assistant level. Also the ward managers wanted to cut down the hours they were spending on the phone arranging temporary staffing.

My vision was to offer a 'one-stop shop' facility. The ward manager would make one call to the team and we would provide nurses with the right skills and abilities. I could see this as a national service, encouraging flexible working in the NHS. Nurses should be able to work flexibly, as part of a bank, wherever they are in the country. If a nurse is relocating, say from Kent to Yorkshire, they would be guaranteed a job and they wouldn't have to leave the NHS. Also, nurses would work to the same consistent standards and procedures across the country. That vision is just starting to come true now.

4. You need commitment

Setting up both organisations has involved a great deal of hard work, and meant tackling a number of difficulties, drawbacks and obstacles. I think most innovations do.

When we won the contract to deliver NHS Direct in August 1998, we were told that April 7 1999 was our 'go live' date. Getting everything ready in time involved such a massive amount of work that it soon became known as our 'drop dead date'.

Some of the toughest times I experienced were when I was trying to market the nurse bank service, at the beginning. This was a humbling experience. I felt like a travelling sales rep, driving from meeting to meeting, explaining my idea to people who would say, 'Well, I'll let you know.' The first year was incredibly hard, and at one point I would quite happily have given it up, but I didn't want to be beaten, I didn't want the sceptics to get me down because I knew it was the right thing to do.

5. Achieve change through co-operation where you can

While you often need to be a little individualistic in order to challenge current practices and achieve change, you also need to be willing and able to work with others, particularly in a large, complex organisation such as the NHS.

One of my main jobs when I started at NHS Direct was talking to key stakeholders, especially other nurse directors and GPs, who would be affected by our activities. In particular, there were issues with neighbouring trusts around recruiting nurses, because there was (and still is) a national nursing shortage. I needed to recruit fifty highly skilled senior nurses. I could offer them flexible working in modern, state of the art accommodation, and the nursing director in the nearest acute trust was concerned that I'd take half his staff. But I wanted to work closely with him and other nurse directors to make sure I didn't do anything that would be detrimental to their services.

I think I was able to win their co-operation because I was a fellow nurse director in the region, and I knew the other nurse directors very well. It was important to maintain these contacts, and make sure I met with the nurse directors regularly, and discussed their concerns. I was also able to offer them help in some areas. For example, it was a time of mergers and organisational change and I was able to say that if people were displaced by organisational changes I might be able to offer those nurses alternative employment. I was also able to offer jobs to nurses who had disabilities, and able to help some nurses into jobs that better met their skills. Being able to see possible two-way benefits is important for gaining co-operation.

I also went out with our medical director to talk to GPs in the area. We went to tell them about the service and tried to help them think about how it could benefit them. Some GPs were very keen – they saw how it could prevent them being woken up unnecessarily at two o'clock in the morning. There were others who were more sceptical.

6. Work on the culture

When I was building the organisation, I wanted a different culture from what I'd found in some other parts of the NHS.

The NHS is a very demanding place to be and part of NHS culture can be about moaning about your lot. Some people wanted to come and work for me because, they said, life was so awful where they were, but it seemed to me that their lives could still be awful if they brought that mentality with them.

When I was recruiting, I was able to start with a clean sheet of paper. I wanted people with the right skills and experience, but I also wanted people with the right attitude, who would be prepared to take action on issues, not just complain about them.

We were still learning and experimenting, and I also needed nurses who were willing to take a leap of faith, who were willing to work without a clear role definition and clear responsibilities. My senior team in particular, who were H-grade nurses, had to be very flexible. To balance the uncertainty I wanted to build a culture that encouraged learning, that supported and valued staff.

This was a new role and needed a new skill set, and we had to expect people to feel some conflicts and disorientation, to ask themselves from time to time: is this really nursing? what am I doing here? I think a learning culture means encouraging people to talk about issues of that kind as they arise. We do a lot of work in the organisation on learning through reflective practice.

Part of building and maintaining that culture has been by managing by walking the floor – what Peters and Waterman (1982) called 'managing by walking about'. The way to get people to work with you is to spend a lot of time talking with them. Managing by walking about means keeping in touch with the nurses, making sure we're moving in the right direction, that they're happy, and if there are issues working out how to solve them. I also want to keep getting their input, using their expertise and ensuring they understand the vision and direction of travel.

With so many flexible workers and part-time workers, it can be difficult to keep everyone informed and involved. Whenever we have a major communication with the team, like at business planning time, we don't just issue a business plan; we try to involve everyone in the writing of the business plan. So when we've set meetings or seminars, we've done that at all times of the day and night to try to include everyone. We also have an email system for every member of staff to access.

We provide a very thorough training programme to assist the nurses in working with patients over the telephone, but part of the learning culture is about ensuring that they feel able to say 'I don't know if I've got that right', and check their decision with the medical director. Nine times out of ten he confirms their decision was correct or he will suggest other courses of action.

One of the best things for me is seeing how the nurses have grown: their IT skills, their communication and intuition skills, and their general knowledge of nursing.

7. Keep experimenting

NHS Professionals is still a young organisation, going through the first flush of development. NHS Direct is older and more mature, but we're still developing and still innovating, and I think that's important.

Once we established the core service, we started experimenting in other areas. We were an early implementer of out-of-hours GP services, for example. At the time of writing, we have partnerships with approximately 250 GPs. Those GPs have seen their home visits drop by an average of 30%. This service continues to grow and develop.

We also tendered for and won a community alarms contract on behalf of social services, monitoring vulnerable people in their own homes. One of the major issues for a hospital, if they have an elderly patient who is going to be discharged, is the carer who may be worried about that elderly patient going home. But now the patient can have an alarm pendant put on, which we can monitor, and if necessary we can ring that person every day. This helps to support the carer.

We will have to keep on experimenting to meet the challenges of maintaining the core service, too. The leadership challenges now are about retention and recruitment. Turnover has been low. Some staff have been with us for two years and they will want to move on – which is healthy. I want to enable people to feel they can move on and develop further, and I also want to make sure we keep the culture we've developed here.

We have deliberately kept a very flat structure, but that presents a challenge, too, because there aren't roles for people to develop into in hierarchical terms. We have developed a competency-based framework that enables people to enhance their skills, so they can develop in different ways, but this hasn't quite filled the gap, because people seem to expect to have a new job title and the status that goes with it.

One interesting experiment that has paid off has been the use of an assessment centre as part of recruitment. We found that when we just used interviews for recruitment, people were being appointed without having a good understanding of the job – even though we thought we were doing a lot of work around explaining the role to them.

We developed a competency model and an assessment centre specifically for NHS Direct. The assessment centre includes interviews and also role-plays and scenarios. We assess the applicants' team-working skills and critical thinking skills – both of which are important for NHS Direct nurses. We take 50% of applicants – a lower proportion than we used to take from the interviews alone – but those we do appoint stay longer and they have a better understanding of the role from the beginning. The assessment centre approach is now being used in many NHS Direct sites now. We give those people who aren't successful in the assessment centre detailed feedback and a development plan they can use to help them think about their next role in the NHS.

Ours was a second-wave NHS Direct pilot site. There wasn't much previous experience, and we had to learn by experimenting. Some things we got right and some things we learnt by our mistakes. The third and fourth wave sites had much more guidance that came from the experiences of the first and second wave sites. Now the core business is established, and some of the additional developments are settling in, there might be a temptation to sit back and stop experimenting, but I would find that very difficult to do.

In a way this seventh point – *keep experimenting* – takes us back to the first one – *take opportunities when they arise, make them when you can* – and we can start moving through the cycle again.

References

Pedler, M., Aspinwall, K. (1998) *A Concise Guide to the Learning Organisation* London: Lemos & Crane.

Pedler, M., Burgoyne, J., Boydell, T. (1996) *The Learning Company: A Strategy for Sustainable Development* London: McGraw-Hill.

Senge, P. M. (1990) *The Fifth Discipline* London: Random House Business Books.

■ Jayne Barnes is Executive Nurse Director of the West Yorkshire Ambulance Service (WYMAS). She helped to develop the flagship NHS Direct service and is also responsible for the development of the innovative temporary staffing service NHS Professionals. She works with the Modernisation Agency and is a member of the Government's Access Task Force. A nurse by profession, she has worked in the National Health Service for the past 23 years.

CHAPTER SIXTEEN

Achieving innovation and complex change – modernisation through creative collaboration

Karen Picking

Introduction

> Thinking of the NHS as a complex evolving system provides an opportunity to develop a more organic approach
>
> > Pratt and Plamping (1998)

Many influences have impacted upon health and social care services over the years, with the result that organisations tend to offer care from their own individual bases and with individualistic perspectives. The NHS Plan encourages staff within the service to modernise to meet future needs of the people and communities. This is a hugely challenging and exciting agenda, especially considering that no one organisation has total responsibility for the service.

At a local level this involves many organisations collaborating to review and modernise services, considering all services as part of a whole system. Partnership is at the heart of this approach. The NHS is a complex evolving system and understanding change in complex adaptive systems is the key to achieving effective modernisation.

This paper considers the science of complexity and how this can be applied to achieving change in NHS and Social Care systems. It outlines a process for achieving such complex change based upon principles for managing complex adaptive systems (Plsek, 1998). This process was used in a significant change project undertaken within Health Promotion Services in Teesside. The learning from this experience has widespread applicability for many services which face the challenge of working in partnership in constantly adaptive systems.

Complexity and creative collaboration

> Today all organisations require creative thinking from every member, not just a few. The world's complexity and pace mean that we can no longer rely on individual leaders and 'Lone Rangers' to solve our problems. Rather we must learn to work together, to identify our own missions, to form our own Great Groups.
>
> Bennis and Biederman (1997)

In recent years thinking around change has moved away from structured change management to more organic adaptive development. This reflects developments in science in general. Fundamental to the newly emerged ideas is the work of Reynolds (1986) who studied the flying and flocking behaviours of birds. As a result of this work we can now consider organisations as components of organic systems where individual parts fly and flock together. By understanding the attractors for flying and the simple rules required to encourage flocking we can understand behaviours to motivate and encourage individuals to embrace change and to work together in evolving their continuously adapting systems. This work has been developed further by Plsek et al (1997) and Gon (2000).

It appears that in complex adaptive systems the collective leaders encourage evolution by working together in partnership. With the help of those working in the system simple rules can be developed, which support order without stifling creativity. Within this framework of simple rules, individuals and groups in the system are freed up to develop creatively. This can motivate individuals and groups to plan and develop their services in partnership. Given space, freedom and support, the various components of the system can fly with positive and renewed energy. Through the collaborative leadership and simple rules the various parts can develop in partnership and become networked. Achieving networked organisations in the NHS and social care is an essential feature of modernisation. These issues are identified and developed by Conner (2001).

Creativity in innovation and change in the NHS is key to modernisation.

Modernising specialist health promotion services Teesside – 2000/2001

> When it comes to creative long-term development of your organisation, let go and let it happen. If you give up trying to know what cannot be known and trying to control what cannot be controlled you will have more energy and feel more secure about participating in the self-organising process that will produce emergent new outcomes for your organisation.
>
> Stacey (1995)

Prior to modernisation, a Tees-wide specialist health promotion service was commissioned by the Health Authority and provided from secondary care. The service had very few links with the four emerging Primary Care Groups in the four main Tees localities. It had therefore become isolated from the core agenda of these localities. The highly qualified professionals who delivered the service were a scarce resource, and they were organised around areas of expertise, specialist knowledge and professional groupings.

There was a high degree of frustration among service users regarding the priorities set by the service. This was matched by a high degree of frustration among the staff, who felt their expertise and resource were not fully utilised. There was a lot of health promotion being undertaken in Teesside throughout the service and also through the Health Action Zone and other initiatives, and this had led to fragmented and uncoordinated activity between agencies and across numerous projects.

Modernisation

Modernisation started in July 2000. Health Promotion was redesigned to meet the future needs of all stakeholders throughout Teesside. There was no lead agency: modernisation was achieved through a partnership approach between four Primary Care Groups/Trusts, Tees Health, North Tees and Hartlepool NHS Trust, four Education Services, four Environment Services, Teesside Health Action Zone, Teesside Public Health Partnership.

Views from all users, agencies, staff, and external good practice influenced the development of the new model of health promotion. The key processes were complex as they involved and engaged numerous agencies and professionals and had many users with very differing needs. In addition the service was adapting from a professionally-led health promotion service to a locality- and community-led health development facility. Rather than promoting healthy lifestyles the emphasis was increasingly shifted towards capacity building within communities to develop skills and resources, behaviours and cultures to develop healthier people. Health Promotion was seen very much as a service within a complex adaptive system.

Approach

Initially a group of the key leaders from each of the main organisations met and identified the need for the review and shared what they would like to see from the service in the future. Individual discussions with key stakeholders and users of the service provided further information on future needs of the service.

The Business Excellence Model (EFQM 2001) provided a useful framework within which to review of the service.

The model provides a means of analysing and developing excellence. It directs attention to nine key areas of an organisation's activity – as shown in Figure 1. The five enablers – leadership, policies and strategies, people within the organisation, partnerships and resources, and processes – produce results of four different kinds – key performance results, staff satisfaction or dissatisfaction, impact on customers, clients or users, and impact on the community. In this project, the model was used to analyse not just a single organisation, but the provision of a service by a partnership of a number of organisations.

The views of staff, stakeholders, and user influenced the future needs of the service. Clearer outcomes were identified. New policies and a new strategy was agreed. New leadership roles were created, partnerships agreed and developed, and people were managed in new multi-agency teams. Key processes were reviewed in partnership. As a result priorities for activity were significantly adjusted.

Staff focus groups were held and staff organisation representatives were involved. A large stakeholder workshop was held and over 100 key people (including many users) were involved in giving their views about the

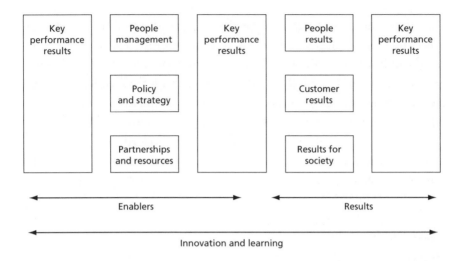

Figure 1: The Business Excellence Model

future service. From this a model of future services emerged. This was discussed by the steering group and key stakeholders, and adapted accordingly, and a programme of change was agreed and facilitated. The partner organisations agreed a new health promotion strategy and new health promotion principles to apply across all Teesside. Within these simple principles new teams were created and given freedom to develop innovative programmes of work. Team development within and across teams was critical to success. It was essential to ensure appropriate networked arrangements for all the parts of the system. All the leaders needed to let the new service and the new teams evolve and continuously develop within the strategy, principles and network.

Outcomes

The need to devolve health promotion to localities became a key feature of how the service was to run. However, a four way split of all resources was not considered effective, because specialist expertise was in short supply. It was also regarded as important that a significant amount of activity should be led and co-ordinated across Teesside, but not necessarily by only one person or one organisation.

The organisations therefore agreed a networked service across Teesside that would be developed by four multi-agency groups that were led, managed and focused at locality level. Each locality developed a multi-agency network that agreed and delivered an innovative, integrated health development programme of work to support local strategic partnership development, neighbourhood renewal, and community plans.

Specialist Tees–wide roles were developed, through structured networking, to maximise the use of specialist expertise and minimise duplication of scarce resource. New roles were created that provided lateral cross-Tees leadership for key specialist aspects of the service.

A specialised, customer-focused, shared resource for Teesside was established, led by one locality on behalf of the whole network. This provided expertise such as graphic design.

Five new teams were established. They were given freedom to develop and to work in new ways, innovate and encourage creative collective collaboration among colleagues from all agencies. Locality innovation workshops were held. Creative innovative programmes of work were agreed for each locality and led by the new teams.

Health Promotion Principles were agreed for everyone working in health promotion in Teesside. These required considerable thought and discussion. Once agreed these simple rules provided the framework for all health promotion activity. All staff reviewed and agreed to adopt the professional code of conduct for Health Promotion Specialists.

A new Health Promotion Strategy for Teesside was agreed based upon the Teesside Health Improvement Programme. A stronger and closer alliance was developed with the enhanced locality Public Health Network in Teesside.

Critical to success was the commitment by all localities to own the agenda, the service and to continuously develop. Users and colleagues observed a considerably higher degree of enthusiasm, excitement and energy from staff in the localities. An organisation development facilitator helped the whole process, and support for a networking workshop was provided by the Northern and Yorkshire Learning Alliance as part of the Northern and Yorkshire Region's approach to modernisation (NYx 2001).

A great deal was achieved in a short time. Activity on modernisation began in July 2000. The new model was agreed by the partnership organisations in October 2000. This was implemented in April 2001. In May 2001 the new teams concentrated upon their development and how they were networked together. Structured networking was developed and reviewed in summer 2001.

Learning

The following learning points were identified by those involved, including views from the leaders, the staff and users.

- Experienced and highly qualified professionals find themselves working very hard in frustrating services designed for a previous NHS system. By re-designing the systems, the skills, expertise and resource can be re-energised and re-focussed for the future Health and Social Care needs
- Partnership leadership of change is essential, requiring collaborative and consensual working
- Involvement of all users, stakeholders and staff valuably informed the outcome and assisted in gaining commitment
- Committed, hard-working staff were surprised in some cases about the views of users and clients
- Innovation was enabled by a willingness and a desire to be radical, and to take some risks
- The effects of change on staff were sometimes greater than the staff and their managers initially realised
- Staff involvement and union partnership working was essential. The organisations had adopted negotiated policies on consultation during change. Direct communication with staff was regarded as important – but some difficulties were encountered in this area during the consultation period. Community-wide human resource policies were required, and partnership working by HR professionals across the agencies was essential
- Managers have greater awareness and sensitivity to staff issues during change
- Implementation is only the beginning. The Tees-wide network is fragile, and the new teams will take time to develop. Staff in the NHS and social care organisations are generally comfortable with and reasonably

good at networking. Whilst networked organisations are regarded as the way forward these are challenging to develop and will take time, commitment, skills and collective leadership

- Simple rules within a framework or strategy enable teams to be given freedom to develop innovative agendas to meet the needs and outcomes of their service
- Leaders do not need to concern themselves with the detail of how each team will work when a strategy, some simple rules and some guiding principles are in place. The need for review, feedback and follow through is an essential collective leadership requirement
- Leaders, staff and users considered it valuable to have the support of a trained facilitator during the process of modernisation

Summary

Health Promotion works within a complex adaptive system. By understanding the principles of achieving change and innovation in complex adaptive systems it was possible to modernise the service across a whole community when no single agency has lead responsibility.

An effective approach to modernisation has emerged. The key features are:

- Collaborative leadership willing to let go and give freedom to innovate to teams of people from all organisations
- Simple rules, strategy and guiding principles are agreed for the service
- Teams are encouraged to work creatively and innovate
- Staff involvement and partnership working
- A networked organisation is developed which recognises continuous adaptation of the complex system within which it operates

This project has given the leaders of health and social care organisations in Teesside a better understanding of the processes of complex change, and confidence that multi-agency partnership change can be achieved. This in turn has led to commitment to further modernisation throughout Teesside. The organisations have gone on to review family planning and reproductive health services, professions allied to medicine, and other services using and adapting this approach.

Throughout the NHS and social care, services are in need of modernisation. The systems are complex. They are constantly adapting. Partnership and collaboration is essential to success in both delivery and modernisation. Confidence to lead and achieve innovation will develop through increased understanding of change in complex adaptive systems. Using this approach to achieve fundamental improvements for patients, users, carers and staff is an exciting challenge.

Acknowledgements

In the spirit of partnership and collaboration I would like to acknowledge the commitment and contributions to collaborative change from all the staff in Health Promotion and the team who led the change: Colin Mcleod, Graeme Oram, Chris Willis, Jon Chadwick, Val Abbas, Paul Johnstone, Pam Cooper, Aidan Mullen, Steve Hunter, Sue Cash, Jim Wilson, Toks Sangowawa.

References

Bennis, Warren, Biederman, Patricia Ward (1997) *Organising Genius – The Secrets of Collaboration* Addison-Wesley Publishing Company, Inc.

Conner, Maxine (2001) 'Developing Network Based Services in the NHS': *International Journal of Health Care Quality Assurance and Management* forthcoming.

EFQM (2001) – the Business Excellence Model can be found at www.efqm.org as at 17 August 2001.

Gon, Sherri M. (2000) 'Thriving on the Edge of Chaos: What Health Care Organisations Can Learn from complexity Science' details at www.medicine21.co/complexity as at 17 August 2001.

NHS Plan (2000): Department of Health: HMSO.

NYx (2001) details of the Northern and Yorkshire Learning Alliance can be found at www.nyx.org.uk as at August 17 2001.

Plsek, Paul E. (1998) 'An Organisation is not a machine – principles for managing complex adaptive systems' Paul E. Plsek and Associates, Inc available through www.directedcreativity.com as at 14 September 2001.

Plsek, Paul, Lindberg, Curt and Zimmerman, Brenda (1997) 'Some Emerging Principles for Managing in Complex Adaptive Systems' Paul E. Plsek and Associates, Inc available through www.directedcreativity.com as at 14 September 2001.

Pratt J., and Plamping D. (1998) 'The NHS – Order for Free' Proceedings from the Organisations as complex systems conference, Warwick: Warwick University 1998 details at www.wholesystems.co.uk

Stacey, Ralph (1995) 'Creativity in Organisations – The importance of Mess' The Business School, University of Hertfordshire.

■ Karen Picking is an Organisation Development Consultant. Her current portfolio includes:

- Board member – Regional modernisation board Northern and Yorkshire Region
- Associate – Northern and Yorkshire Learning Alliance
- Associate – TUC Partnership Institute
- Associate – British Association of Medical Managers

She was the Director of Organisation Development, South Tees Acute Hospitals NHS Trust facilitating organisation development from 1991–2000. karen@kpicking.fsnet.co.uk

Index